Scenarios in American Government

Scenarios in American Government

SONDRA L. RICAR

Chandler Sharp Publishers, Inc.
NOVATO, CALIFORNIA

Chandler Sharp Publishers, Inc.
11 Commercial Boulevard, Ste. A
Novato, CA 94949

ISBN 0-88316-579-1

Library of Congress Cataloging-in-Publication Data

Ricar, Sondra L., 1962–.
    Scenarios in American government / Sondra L. Ricar.
        p. cm.
    Includes an index.
    ISBN-13: 978-0-88316-579-9
    ISBN-10: 0-88316-579-1
1. United States—Politics and government. I. Title.
    JK275.R53 2006
    320.473—dc22
                        2006010614

Copyeditor: Judy Weiss
Text design and composition: Hiatt & Dragon
Cover design: Stewart Cauley, Pollendesign

Printed in the USA

Contents

4   When Rights Conflict: Civil Rights and Disibilities   45

Congresswoman Dustman was elected in part due to the strong support of the firefighters' union. Now representatives from that union are asking her to sponsor an amendment that would dramatically change the Americans with Disabilities Act, limiting the rights of persons with disabilities to save the lives of others. The congresswoman must decide whose rights should prevail when rights conflict and issues of equality are at stake.

5   Having Our Say: Public Opinion   59

Governor Turner is a novice in politics. He won on a platform of public control, pledging to abide by public opinion in all major policy decisions. Party politicians are frustrated with his reliance on polls and attempt to educate him on the problems associated with letting public opinion guide decision making. How should politicians evaluate public opinion, and what is the nature of public opinion in a democracy?

6   Culture in a Country of Immigrants: Political Socialization   73

Pat Richardson and her family are going to dinner at the grandparents' house. There they have a long conversation about the problems facing the country, showing the different opinions and beliefs of three generations, exploring the ways in which Americans are socialized, and highlighting the problems associated with diverse political cultures co-existing in the United States.

7   Smoke-Filled and Other Rooms: Interest Groups   89

Senator Keim is thinking about the best way to reform interest groups to prevent the appearance of impropriety. She experiments with this reform by having a meeting with competing interest groups in her office while discussing a bill that she must decide whether to support. The discussion raises questions relating to the nature of representation in a democracy and examines proposals for limiting the potential for corruption associated with interest groups.

8   A Dime's Worth of Difference?: Political Parties   103

A BBC report on the primary elections in America explores the problems facing political parties, compares aspects of our system to Britain's, and outlines proposed reforms to improve the U.S. electoral system. The program discusses the weakness of political parties, federalism as it relates to political parties, and the problems of campaign funding in elections. It also explores the strengths of political parties and the roles they play in the U.S. system.

9 Selling Candidates: Campaigns and Elections   117
Professor David Wiley's political science class is bored with the lecture, so he
initiates a class discussion. The students try to resolve problems associated with
the Electoral College, campaign funding, low voter turnout, and other topics
related to campaigns and elections.

10 Shooting the Messenger: The Media   133
Mr. Murtock, a TV station manager, must make some difficult decisions about
stories to air on this week's news magazine. One reporter has filmed a story
about a guerilla movement that seems to present America in a bad light, and
another reporter has a story about a serial killer that the police do not want
aired. The reporters and editors argue the merits of the stories and the proper
role of the media in our system.

11 The People's Talking Shop: Congress   147
Senator Witowski has decided to filibuster a popular bill, arguing that it is not
in the best interests of society. His filibuster raises questions about the filibuster, amendments that are not germane, and the role of a representative in a
democracy.

12 Hail to the Chief: The Presidency   161
Charles must meet with the three members of his dissertation committee to
explain some controversial recommendations he is making about the presidency. He raises questions about the "natural born" clause, candidates who hold
dual citizenship, the pardon, and whether the Constitution allows women to
become president.

13 Cutting Red Tape: The Bureaucracy   175
The president's campaign included a promise to reform the bureaucracy. Sheldon is the man in charge of doing so, and he must explain to the president the
problems he faces and why it is not easy to rid the bureaucracy of inefficiency
and waste.

14 Who Will Judge the Judge?: The Judiciary   189
Jorge Escalente is the newest justice on the United States Supreme Court. His
breakfast meeting with colleagues raises issues about judicial review, the role
of personal beliefs in judicial decision-making, and political ideology influencing federal judges. Also explored is the appearance of impropriety in the election of state judges.

Introduction

For the student:

Government is boring. It doesn't affect my life. There is nothing I can do to affect government. There is no reason for me to study it. All too often students express feelings like this about American government.

While these feelings have some validity, it is my contention that the fundamental premises are wrong. American government is dynamic, interesting, and affects the lives of people throughout this country and the rest of the world. The fact that the government requires you to take a class in American government should be enough impetus for you to want to study the subject, if for no other reason than to ask why? By what right does the government tell me I must study this subject?

Unfortunately, most students never bother asking these questions and therefore never come to fully appreciate the many ways the government impacts their lives. Students then endure a semester of learning about a subject that they find boring and carry these negative attitudes about government throughout their lives.

Part of the reason students do not ask these questions is that they find the subject boring. Textbooks are written in a style that is either inaccessible or so scholarly as to bore the average student—and they often seem to evade discussion of actual political controversies rather than clarify the different positions involved and illuminate the issues. This book is an attempt to address these problems.

Scenarios in American Government starts from the premise that government plays a crucial role in our lives and that therefore what government does is interesting. The fundamental issues of American government and politics are explored throughout the book in the context of debates on contemporary issues that often divide Americans.

This text is composed of short fictional stories relating to current events and core ideas in American government. These stories illustrate political concepts in a way that will help you understand the fundamental issues under discussion and relate them to everyday life. The events are imaginary; as this book went to press there had not yet been a terrorist attack on either the Statue of Liberty or Las Vegas, ectogenesis was not a viable alternative to abortion, and the United Nations was not considering a worldwide program to end terrorism. However, these stories will help you to understand the ways in which government works and affects our lives. This is therefore a critical thinking text. There are no right or wrong answers to the questions raised by the book. Many of the stories simply stop. You must decide for yourself how the situation in the story should be resolved.

One of the themes of this book is the complexities of governing this vast country. For every possible solution to a problem, there are drawbacks that we must consider. Each chapter is followed by "points to ponder," provocative statements meant to challenge your thinking. It is far too easy for most Americans to criticize the actions taken by our government in any given situation. This book puts you in the situation of making governmental decisions—and you'll find that it is not easy to resolve the problems presented here. For every possible solution there are additional problems that need to be addressed.

There is also the presumption in our society that in almost any politically contentious situation, there is only one right answer. Whatever your stance on subjects like abortion, affirmative action, or the rights of accused terrorists, there is a tendency to believe that those who hold the opposite stance are automatically wrong. This book presents both sides of an issue to help you see the valid points made by the other side. By looking at both sides you might change your mind about a position you previously held; but you will certainly better understand your own position. It is only when you have thoroughly explored all aspects of a question that you can claim to hold an educated opinion on a subject.

This book assumes that you know relatively little about American government. It is intended to be used in conjunction with a standard American government textbook. *Scenarios* also presumes that you will one day be an adult faced with decisions about life and politics. Many of you are not prepared to make difficult decisions, since no one has taught you how to evaluate evidence, analyze arguments, and weigh the pros and cons of an action. After reading several chapters in this book you will find that you are much better prepared to make tough decisions about complex problems.

As you read *Scenarios*, put yourself in the position of a government leader and come to your own conclusions about how these issues should be resolved. Assume that you are part of the next generation of leaders of this country—since that in fact is the case. You need to learn the skills that are necessary for you to perform that role, whether as a member at some level of our government, a business owner, or a parent deciding how to vote for members of the board of your child's school. One day you will be faced with situations like the ones discussed here, and you will need the skills that this book helps you develop.

To the instructor:

This book is written in order to help you get your students involved in American government. It is specifically designed to help develop critical thinking skills among your students. The fictional aspect of the stories bothers some professors. However, the rationale I use is the fact that I want my students to struggle with the situations government faces. If I had used actual events, students would simply research the issue, find out how it had been resolved, and present the solution. That type of book does help students develop research skills, but it does not help them develop critical thinking skills, which I have found are sorely lacking among today's students. Also, at a very fundamental level, students do not find past events compelling. These stories present the issues in such a way that students find them enjoyable to read and debate.

This book addresses the full spectrum of American government, from the Constitution and federalism, through civil liberties and civil rights, to the institutions of American government, political parties, interest groups, and other topics covered in the standard American government text. Unlike most supplementary books for American government courses, this one builds on itself. Federalism is introduced in the chapter on the Constitution and covered extensively in its own chapter, but is also brought up in chapters on public opinion, political parties, and other chapters. This helps students see how things they learned early in the semester relate throughout the term. Because these subjects interested them with their coverage of current events, they remember the main points when they come up later. The separation of powers, congressional oversight, and the role of the media are other topics that recur throughout the reader.

At the same time, each of the stories can stand alone, so if the textbook you use does not follow the same chapter sequence in this book, it is easy to assign the chapters out of order. Likewise, some textbooks combine some of these topics. You can either assign both chapters from the book or choose which chapter you wish your students to read without adversely affecting their understanding of the issues.

There are some things to keep in mind while teaching from these stories. First of all, don't let the students get bogged down in the details. For example, in the chapter on the Constitution, the story introduces a new form of technology for validating a person's identity. Do not spend a great deal of time discussing whether or not it is technologically feasible. That is not the point. The issue is whether or not we should have to prove our identity to the government. Likewise, I do not let my students assume that our government's options are limited by history. I encourage my students to imagine they were the ones making these decisions, and I continuously remind them that no Supreme Court decision is engraved in marble. I tell them that while it is true that our government rests on a body of law and relies on previous Supreme Court decisions to guide government action, the cases in the reader encourage students to think for themselves, not rely on Court decisions. After all, the Supreme Court can change the law whenever justices vote to do so by overturning a previous decision—as illustrated by the *Brown v. Board of Education* school desegregation case of 1954. The exercise here is for the students to decide, not for them to research what has been done in the past. This is not to say that Supreme Court decisions are unimportant; they are. However, there is a high likelihood that in the near future the Supreme Court will overturn *Roe v. Wade*, the decision that legalized abortion, or declare laws regarding campaign financing unconstitutional.

Some may wonder why the book's chapters cover so many topics. In the chapter about the presidency, for example, the qualifications of the president, the roles of the president, and issues of gender in this country are covered. However, you can choose which issues you would like your students to address in the discussions or papers. Finally, as you teach from this text, you will find yourself asking, "But what about. . ." You will wonder why I left certain obvious solutions out of the story. I did this for two reasons. First, I did not want to give the students a simple answer; I want them to struggle with the issue. Second, I want the professor to have a role in the process. After the students have debated an issue, I bring up what was left out of the reader to see if they agree or disagree with the way most experts would solve the problem.

These stories encourage the students to discuss and debate the issues. The discussions are a crucial part of this process. Either a full class discussion or small group discussions help the students understand the issues and develop not only critical thinking skills but listening skills, since they must listen to others' opinions on these topics and evaluate them. It can be helpful to have the students jot down their responses to the points to ponder before the discussion. After they have discussed these issues with the class, they can then go back and respond to the points again, explaining why they did or did not change their minds. You will find that your students are much more interested in American government and more willing to engage in the discussions through the use of this book.

Chapter I

"All Necessary Powers"?: The Constitution

The image on the television monitor was stark. Amid the smoking ruins, a large American flag was flying defiantly. The camera pulled back, focusing on the president standing somberly in front of the ruins.

"My fellow Americans, I speak to you today from Liberty Island, where the Statue of Liberty is still smoldering. Last week, as you know, the statue, a symbol of our nation known throughout the world, was destroyed by terrorists. The Basque Liberation Army has claimed credit, citing our support of the Spanish government in their fight against the Basques. As a result of this attack, as well as that in New York on September 11, 2001, and on Las Vegas last year by remnants of al-Qaeda, I am issuing an order to the appropriate elements of the federal bureaucracy. Let me emphasize that this order is being issued in the interests of national security after extensive discussions with the attorney general, the secretary for homeland security, and members of the Joint Chiefs of Staff. My order is as follows: By midnight, May 30, 2010, six months from today, every American citizen will be required to carry a national identity card. This card will carry information such as birthplace and date, Social Security number, and home address, and it will also carry a unique, DNA-based identifier. The persons responsible for designing these cards tell me that it will be impossible for them to be forged, due to this new DNA-based identifier. During times of national emergency, this card will help to identify American citizens and enable the law enforcement agencies of this country to track down foreign-born terrorists.

"I realize that this is a radical step for our country. However, we must enable our law enforcement agencies to rapidly distinguish citizen from foreigner in times of emergency like the one we find ourselves in now. We now know that some of the terrorists escaped in the immediate aftermath of the explosion by posing as innocent American citizens. We must not allow this to happen again. As your president, it is my responsibility to take every conceivable precaution to safeguard the lives of Americans. This national identity card is, in my opinion, a relatively benign way to accomplish this goal.

"I join you in your prayers for those lost at this monument. Let us do everything possible to ensure that they are the last Americans to give their lives in a foreign-based terrorist attack on this country. Thank you, and goodnight." As the camera drew back, President Crockett gazed determinedly at it, as if trying to show that nothing would harm the country again. Immediately, the news analyst turned to those in the studio. Jack Edmunds, news anchor for American Media Market, swiveled to face the man on his left, saying, "Senator Rush, your thoughts on this radical new proposal."

"Well, Jack, as you know, we in Congress were just informed of the new policy this morning. My colleagues and I have not had much time to study it, but our first concern is whether or not the president has the power to institute such a program. The White House claims that it does have this power, based on the 2009 revision to the USA Patriot Act of 2007. That act, as you will remember, gives the president 'all necessary powers to fight foreign terrorist attacks.' In his interpretation, the faithfully executed clause of the Constitution gives him the power to institute a national identity card program to fight attacks by foreign terrorists. Many of us in Congress disagree. The faithfully executed clause does allow the president to interpret the laws passed by Congress. But when we revised the Patriot Act, the intent was to increase our security through traditional methods. A national identity card is a radical departure from traditional beliefs in this country. President Crockett is violating the separation of powers principle. It should be up to Congress to implement an identity card if we feel it is necessary. We will be holding hearings beginning next week to determine whether or not this new policy exceeds the president's powers."

"Somehow, Senator, that is not surprising," said the anchorman dryly. "However, you don't seem to find the idea of the national identity card troublesome, just the fact that the president seems intent on implementing the system without prior authorization of Congress. Many people find the whole idea of the national identity card repulsive. What do you think, Janine Aliton, as a representative of the ACLU?"

"Frankly, Jack, I'm bothered by the whole idea. Like the senator, I'm unsure whether the president actually has the constitutional power to implement such a program. I also have doubts about the constitutionality of a system of national identity cards. Such a system reeks of totalitarian government and is anathema to many Americans. My maternal grandparents were refugees from the Soviet Union. Through national identity cards, the Soviet government was able to infringe on many aspects of its citizens' lives. This is not something we feel comfortable with here in America."

"Hold on now, Janine," interrupted Steven Stitler, the White House spokesperson. "This government has no intention of tracking or spying on American citizens. The identity cards are essential to national security. You know as well as I do the problems facing law enforcement in this country today. Security at many of our national monuments, at big events like the Super Bowl, at airports, is extremely difficult. With this system, law enforcement can pass American citizens through security and concentrate their efforts on those who are not citizens. This would be a means of easing life for American citizens and allowing law enforcement to scrutinize the rest of the people for terrorist affiliations. It would also solve a major problem. Despite the reforms after September 11, 2001, the computers at the FBI, CIA, and INS still can't talk to one another.

This program would include the development of a centralized database for important information and also fund new computer systems for all aspects of the federal government, enabling the different departments to share information."

"But Steven," Jack Edmunds jumped back into the discussion, "this would seem to discriminate against noncitizens. It also would not have stopped a Timothy McVeigh. Keep in mind that although the last three terrorist acts in this country have been perpetrated by foreigners, we do have militia groups here. I can see the possibility of this program inciting domestic terrorism by some of the militia groups, which already feel the government is doing too much to take away their privacy."

"No program is perfect," replied Steven, "and we are attempting to defuse the militia groups through other means. The bottom line is that we must do everything possible to prevent further foreign-based terrorist acts in this country. I believe many Americans would be willing to give up a little of their privacy in return for security."

"Janine Aliton, what do you reply to that?" asked the anchor, a slight smirk on his face.

"I agree that no program is perfect, and I also agree with you, Jack, that this program is discriminatory. Noncitizens who are legally in this country would be targeted by law enforcement. The vast majority of them are innocent of any crime. I disagree with Steven; I don't think the majority of Americans will sit still for this kind of government intrusion in their lives. This program also says nothing about legal resident aliens. Where would they fit in? Would they also be subject to intense police scrutiny? I also wonder about the information on these cards. You may say that they will only contain state information that the government already has, but I wonder. Will these cards state religion, as a way of tracking possible Muslim terrorists? Will they include information on criminal background? Wouldn't the government like to know, at public events or in sensitive locations, if a person has a history of involvement in militias or supremacist groups? And what about travel history? If I had a history of traveling to places where there are a lot of terrorists, would that be noted on my card?"

Steven interrupted before Janine could answer: "I know the ACLU is concerned about protecting the rights of all people in America. Let me ask you this: Suppose when you leave here today you stop at a mall to do some shopping. There are a large number of elderly ladies at the mall. Just as you walk into a store you hear shots being fired. Those twenty white-haired little old ladies had pulled out Uzis and were killing people. What are you going to do the next time you see a group of little old ladies? It is unfortunate, but sometimes law enforcement must use profiles. In fact, they would be derelict in their duty if they did not. Just as we test only women, not men, to see if they are transmitting illegal narcotics to an unborn fetus, law enforcement does sometimes need to target specific groups.

"So yes, noncitizens would face greater scrutiny; they already do. It is unfortunate for them, but more than 10,000 Americans have died at the hands of noncitizen terrorists in this country over the last five years. If the government doesn't act, it is not doing its job. The administration has been talking about the problem of legal resident aliens. One of the suggestions that has been made is to have a card for them also, but with a different-colored border. Resident aliens might be subject to greater scrutiny than citizens, but less scrutiny than foreign visitors."

Janine looked at Steven thoughtfully. "Your example is not quite appropriate, Steven. Of course law enforcement shouldn't test men to see if they're transmitting illegal drugs to a fetus. But are you saying that it is appropriate for law enforcement to test all women for illegal drugs to make sure they're not transmitting them to the fetus? Or only all pregnant women? The Supreme Court has disagreed with this position in the past. And by the same logic, you're saying that if a woman is raped, then all men should provide a DNA sample to find the rapist. Our political and judicial systems do not work that way.

"I agree with you that terrorism is a serious problem in this country. And you do make some valid points. But we have the Constitution for a reason. Our Founding Fathers were afraid of government going too far. I think this is an example of what they feared. They wanted to limit government for a reason. Giving too much power to the national government creates problems. In addition to discriminating against noncitizens, there are other problems with these cards.

"I'm concerned, for example, about the DNA-based identifier. For this system to work there will have to be a centralized databank of the DNA of every American citizen. Who will have access to this databank? Will it be used solely to check identity at security screenings, or will law enforcement agencies be able to access it to investigate crimes? Will insurance companies find a way to access this information before granting health insurance? There are troubling questions here."

Jack Edmunds turned to Chris Colter and asked, "What are your thoughts, Chris?"

"Janine made a good point. The Founding Fathers did limit our government. However, they could never have envisioned the terrorist attacks against this country. We need to consider dramatically amending the Constitution to eliminate certain individual rights, like privacy rights and the rights of the Fifth Amendment, so more people like me won't end up burying their husbands. We also need an amendment that says that noncitizens are not covered by the Constitution or Bill of Rights. As it is, the Supreme Court has said that even admitted terrorists have all the protections of the Constitution and Bill of Rights. It is fundamentally wrong that they can attack our country and institutions and still be protected by our laws."

Before Jack could say anything, Janine jumped back in. "I'm sorry for your loss, Chris, but I don't think we should jump to the conclusion that we should start limiting rights in this country. That would create even more trouble. Why not also advocate getting rid of habeas corpus? Let the government throw suspected terrorists in jail and never hold a trial— that's what happened after the attacks on the World Trade Center, with the detainees at Guantánamo Bay."

Chris shook her head. "By what logic do you defend the right of foreign terrorists to all of the same protections as American citizens? It's like you want to give the mugger the gun he needs to mug you with. These people are using our system against us. There is something fundamentally wrong with that. If the FBI catches a terrorist, they can't even question him without an attorney. I say we should torture that person to get information if we have to. Homeland Security knew something was planned before this bombing. Obviously they had an informant or something. Why shouldn't we have taken that person, used truth serum, torture, something, to find out what was being planned so we could prevent this latest atrocity?"

Janine smiled at Chris. "Again, I'm sorry for your loss. But the reason that everyone on American soil is protected by the Constitution is based on our history of being a political haven for people from all over the world. Our ancestors came to this country for political freedom, the freedom to try to make the world better. If we deny constitutional protections to the terrorists, we become no better than they are. We also help the terrorists accomplish their goals, by showing that our freedoms are not absolute."

The senator and the White House spokesperson watched the two women, but before either could speak, Chris replied rapidly, "The Constitution and the principles it embodies will do us no good if we're dead. I am a law-abiding citizen. If the FBI wants to listen to my phone conversations, read my email, or even search my house, I don't care. If that can help stop future terrorist attacks, I'm willing to allow it. Keep in mind, our government has been trying since September 11, 2001, to stop terrorists from attacking us, and it hasn't worked. We've made it too difficult for the government to do its job. I also see no problem with a national DNA databank. This would help solve crimes, and if you've done nothing wrong, what do you have to worry about?"

"Senator, you've been quiet. What are you thinking?" Edmunds tried to draw the senator back into the discussion.

"I have to admit, points have been raised that my colleagues and I had not considered. In our preliminary discussions, we have been focusing on whether or not the president actually has the power to implement such a program, or whether it should be up to Congress to authorize national identity cards. While I agree with Ms. Aliton that there would be some discrimination, I can tell you that I personally have received a lot of feedback from my constituents regarding national security. I tend to agree with Steven that the majority of Americans, like Ms. Colter here, would give up a little privacy in return for safety. I also don't think that the majority of Americans would worry about law enforcement accessing the database to solve crimes. We would have to ensure that the information remained only in the hands of law enforcement. I agree that insurance companies should not be able to access the database. I don't think we need to dramatically alter the Constitution, though. History has shown that when we suspend protections of individual rights, innocent people do suffer. There are also questions about how to pay for these cards. It will be a costly investment, as we would need not only the cards themselves, and the databank, but also the mobile readers to verify the DNA identifier."

"Hold it right there, Senator," Steven intervened. "Although the president didn't raise it in his speech, funding has already been discussed. There will be a tax placed on all foreigners who enter this country legally, for example at airports. It will be collected by customs inspectors. It will go to pay for the cards and all costs associated with them. At the time of entry into the country, all foreigners will also give their fingerprints and a DNA sample. This will help to find criminals and keep known terrorists out of this country. Keep in mind, it will also stimulate sectors of the economy. Businesses will compete to develop cheaper card readers. And before Ms. Aliton interrupts, let me make something clear: The guard at the Super Bowl will not get your entire history. What will happen is that when asked for your card, you will swipe it like you swipe your credit card in a grocery store. You will then insert your finger into the machine, and a cell will be scraped off. The machine will compare the DNA from the cell and card with the DNA in the databank. If all three match, you're cleared and the machine says 'approved,' just as with your credit card. All three must match, so this means that identity theft will become a thing of the past."

"Really, Steven!" exclaimed Janine. "Do you think foreign-born terrorists are just going to come in by plane and give us this information? And other foreigners, who are not terrorists but value their privacy, what do you think they'll do? Is it possible that they'll come to this country illegally? As it is now, we can't protect our borders and keep illegals out of the country."

"Janine, you're under the mistaken impression that we still have privacy in this world. With all of the technological advances and databanks, no one really has any privacy anymore. Also, you're ignoring some of the other benefits from these cards. We would be able to identify fathers so they'd be required to pay child support. The cards would also help in an accident, because the medical history would be readily available. As we develop the process, we will also code the cards with security clearances, so that someone who has no problems in their background would get a higher security clearance than someone with a criminal background. The cards would be updated every five years, so they'd be current. There is a lot of social good that can come out of these cards." Steven looked pleadingly at Janine, almost begging her to agree with him.

Janine shook her head. "Can you tell me with good faith that after the emergency the government will abandon these cards? Or will they become an accepted part of life? The information that the FBI is currently compiling on our emails, reading habits, and so forth—is that going to be put on the cards or in the databank? Is this going to be a way for the IRS to catch people who haven't paid their taxes? If I go to an airport and I haven't paid my taxes, will that show up on my card and will security then take me to jail? You're shaking your head, but aren't these valid questions?"

Before Steven could answer, the anchor jumped in, trying to regain control of the discussion. "Another thing, Steven, is the concern that the government is just using this to introduce the idea of implanted computer chips. Before you laugh, you do realize that some parents are implanting chips in their children, don't you? I can see the government arguing that too many people are losing their cards, so we should go to chips."

Steven shook his head. "Everyone is taking this too far. We're just trying to provide some security for the country."

Jack Edmunds turned to Senator Rush. "Senator, I would like to return to your major concern for a moment. Who does have the authority to implement such a program? I'm not a constitutional scholar, but it does seem to me that the president would have such authority under the re-vised Patriot Act. What do you think, Janine?"

"Jack, as you know, my area of specialization is the Bill of Rights. How-ever, I feel the Constitution is not clear on this issue. Congress writes the laws, and it is up to the president to faithfully execute the laws. This elastic clause is the problem. To faithfully execute the law, in my mind, the president must determine what Congress intended when writing the law. If Congress intended to give the president all power to fight foreign terrorism in this country, then the president probably has the power to implement this proposal."

Jack gave the camera his "thoughtful" look. "Couldn't the Supreme Court rule on this question? That would solve the immediate problem."

"Unfortunately, Jack, our system doesn't work that way. The judicia-ry can only step in when someone can prove they've been harmed. So once the identity card system goes into operation, it can be challenged in court. And, given the mood of the Supreme Court in these troubled times, combined with their historic reluctance to limit the power of the federal government in national security matters, I doubt the Court would put a stop to these cards," Janine replied sourly.

"But you're focusing on the cards themselves. I was wondering if the Court could decide who had the authority to implement the program, Congress or the president," Jack came back rapidly. He hated it when people did not address the issue he had raised.

"I suppose it is feasible that some members of Congress could sue the president for harming them by usurping Congressional powers," Janine replied, "but I am more concerned about the whole idea of the cards. It just seems to fly in the face of what it means to be an American."

"Thanks for outlining your position for us, Janine. We are now being joined by Annabelle Moore, distinguished constitutional scholar. Anna-belle, what do you have to say about the issues that have been raised here tonight?"

"First of all, Jack, thank you for inviting me to join this discussion. Let me say that, from an historical perspective, President Crockett probably can go ahead with his national identity card program. During times of national emergency the Constitution tends to fall by the wayside. We saw this during the Civil War when Lincoln suspended habeas corpus, during the First World War when Wilson used the government to set prices, and, of course, during the Second World War when Japanese Americans were interned. Presidents can disregard the Constitution if Congress lets them."

"What do you mean, if Congress lets them? What can Congress do to stop the president, other than holding hearings or possibly filing a lawsuit?" Jack put on his mystified look for the audience. "Both of these courses of action are clearly within the realm of Congress but would take time. What could Congress do?"

"Jack, too often we make things harder than they are. Yes, Congress can and should hold hearings; that is part of their oversight responsibility, part of checks and balances. But part of the separation of powers is the fact that no one branch of government can work independently. Congress today can do the same thing that past Congresses have done when they disliked a presidential program, what Congress in fact did do toward the end of the Vietnam War: they can cut off the funding. The Constitution gives Congress sole power of appropriation. The president cannot implement this new program without funding. All Congress has to do is refuse to allocate the funding. By law, the president cannot use funds from another program to fund a new program. This is the way Congress can control a president. As we know, Congress has sometimes refused to withhold funding; they funded the internment camps, for example. But if Congress really feels this program is wrong and is willing to take the political heat for opposing it, they can prevent the president from implementing the national identity card system."

The anchor nodded his head, looking sagely at the camera. Annabelle always made him look good. She continued speaking after taking a sip of water.

"But, Jack, there is another potential problem here that needs to be studied. And that is states' rights." She paused again as Jack looked puzzled for the audience. Annabelle went on, "The Tenth Amendment reserves to the states those powers not given to the national government.

I can envision governors arguing that this is a matter for the states to pursue themselves, that they have the right to issue these cards, just like driver's licenses. Now, the federal government will argue that this is a national government matter, like passports. But passports are for foreign travel. These cards essentially would be like a domestic passport, and I can see where there would be an argument that the federal government does not have the power to issue such cards. Keep in mind that various cities and states refused to support some provisions of the original Patriot Act and refused to help the federal government implement some of the programs associated with it. In order to compile these cards and this database, the federal government would need a great deal of help from the state governments. States could simply refuse to cooperate."

"Now wait a minute, Annabelle," interrupted Jack, "surely the federal government can do whatever it needs to in order to protect us from terrorism."

"Not quite, Jack," Annabelle smiled. "The wording of the revised Patriot Act, like the original, is so vague that many citizens are upset. They are pressuring their state governments, and this new card system would give state governments the perfect case to test the limits of the federal government. You need to keep in mind that the states are part of the checks and balances of our system."

"Well, Annabelle, as always, you've put your finger on the crux of the matter. We will have to see how Congress and the states decide to respond," concluded the anchorman.

Annabelle interrupted him. "Jack, there is one other thing I would like to address . . ."

Jack, startled out of his traditional closing, turned to her. "What is it?" he asked abruptly.

"Given the problems our society currently faces, the fear and the uneasiness, I think the media has a duty to act responsibly, to remind Americans why their liberties are being restricted," began Annabelle.

Jack jumped in, "We are acting responsibly. This program is an example of that. We're showing the American people what the government is doing and explaining the possible problems."

"Yes," replied Annabelle, "you are doing that. But the airwaves belong to the public, and we have the right to expect you to sometimes do what is right rather than concentrate on pleasing your advertisers. No, let me finish, Jack. I'm a big sports fan, and it really bothers me that the broadcast media no longer show the national anthem before sporting events. Instead they cut to commercials. As long as we are at war with terrorists, I feel that the media should show the performance of the anthem to remind people of those we have lost and those who are putting their lives on the line while we relax, watching a game. Can you give me a good reason why you can't show the anthem?" Jack glared at Annabelle. "I'm sorry, but we've gone over our allotted time. We'll have to discuss this another time. Thank you, America, and goodnight."

Points to Ponder

Agree or disagree with the following statements, and give your reasons:

1. A system of national identity cards would be a good idea. It would help law enforcement and would not seriously impact our privacy. After all, the government already has most of the information that would be included on such cards.

2. The constitutional separation of powers was a good idea when implemented but today causes confusion and unnecessary gridlock. We need a government that can function rapidly.

3. It would be better if the Supreme Court gave advisory opinions. This way we would know if a proposed law or program would pass constitutional scrutiny.

4. Sometimes it is acceptable for the government to discriminate against a group of people, like legal aliens in this scenario.

5. Often the separation of powers and the system of checks and balances do not work, as in some of the historical cases mentioned by Annabelle. Usually it is because Congress is unwilling to oppose a program that is wrong but enjoys popular support.

6. During a national emergency, it is understandable that the government will infringe on citizen's rights. When the government decides the emergency is over, things go back to normal.

7. Congress sometimes intentionally writes vague laws, like the Patriot Act, so as not to have to take responsibility for unpopular programs.

8. Almost every modern president has tried at one time or another to exceed the powers given him by the Constitution. The demands placed on the president today make that inevitable.

9. The media are not acting responsibly by fulfilling the role given them by the Founders. They are supposed to be a part of our system of checks and balances but often fail to address issues of importance regarding our government.

10. The Constitution is too limiting of our government, preventing the government from effectively fighting terrorism. We need to amend it as Chris indicates.

11. We should allow the government to use torture to get information from suspected terrorists.

12. We need to keep limits on the government, as the Founders envisioned. Otherwise the government will violate our fundamental rights.

Essay Questions

1. Discuss the problems associated with the separation of powers and checks and balances. Is this system of government outmoded or a protection of our rights? Use examples from this story to illustrate your points.

2. Explore the philosophy of the Constitution and our protections, discussing why our rights and limitations on governmental power should or should not extend to all those on U.S. soil, including any who might be here illegally and planning to harm this country.

Chapter 2

Laboratories of Democracy?:
The States and Federalism Today

Representative Karl Cushman looked at Professor Elaine Burman and sighed. This was going to be difficult, but if he could win her over to his point of view, she would be a formidable ally.

"Professor Burman, thank you for sparing me your time," said Karl.

"It's my pleasure, Congressman," replied Elaine. "It's not often that a member of Congress asks to see me on a matter of 'grave importance,' as your aide put it."

Karl smiled at the professor, saying, "Well, I do feel the issue is important, and as you're the recognized authority on federalism, I thought you might be the one to help me. Please understand, I've been through law school and passed the bar, and I've worked in government for years, so I'm not being obtuse when I ask this question." He paused, and the professor nodded at him to show she understood. Karl continued, "Can you explain to me the constitutional basis for states opposing a national criminal code that would eliminate state criminal codes?"

Elaine looked mystified. She shook her head gently, saying, "I'm not sure I understand your question. We have federal criminal codes, and national law is supreme. When there is a conflict between a national law and a state law, over medical marijuana, for example, the United States Supreme Court will eventually resolve the dispute."

"I know that," replied Karl. "But that is the problem, from my point of view. Or at least part of the problem. I'm bothered by the fact that we often spend years and countless dollars resolving issues like that. It can take many years for a case to get to the Supreme Court. When it rules, the decision affects the entire country, and thus the law is uniform. But often the Court refuses to take a case; that leaves confusion and different standards throughout the country.

"But I'm also bothered by the fact that laws differ so much, not just from state to state, but from county to county within some states. For example, the legal age of consent varies from one state to another. In parts of Nevada prostitution is legal, while in other parts it is illegal. And it is offensive that if I commit first degree murder in California I face the death penalty, but if I commit the same crime in Vermont the most I face is life imprisonment without parole. It seems to me that for us to truly be a nation, our criminal laws should be uniform. If I'm traveling or move, I shouldn't have to consult an attorney to ensure that I won't be breaking any laws by engaging in behavior that was routine when I was somewhere else. Like hanging my clothes on a clothesline. That's illegal in some communities. It's absurd."

The professor looked at the congressman thoughtfully, wondering privately how he could have been elected to national office, let alone graduate from law school, without understanding something so basic. She sighed, saying, "The Constitution gives specific powers to the national government, and the Tenth Amendment reserves all other powers to the states or the people. The Founders viewed the states as laboratories of democracy. If it turns out that legalizing prostitution in certain counties of Nevada actually works better than keeping it illegal, if, for example, the prostitutes are less likely to have STDs, or be beaten or killed, or to rob their clients, then the laboratories-of-democracy theory says the rest of the country will eventually legalize prostitution. The Founders did not like the idea of arbitrary measures taken by the national government impacting the lives of people in disparate parts of the country."

"I know that," said Karl impatiently. "But unfortunately, things have not worked out that way. The experiment with legalized prostitution has shown many benefits, but the people of Nevada have not decided to adopt this policy statewide. Needless to say, no other states have adopted it either. While the 'laboratories of democracy' have helped develop innovative social programs, like welfare, I don't think they have found a solution for the problems associated with crime. The bottom line is that a national criminal code would help hold us together as a nation. We still tend to think of ourselves as people from a particular state, not as Americans. Fundamentally, governments were formed to protect people from crime. Think about Hobbes, Locke, political philosophers who dramatically influenced the framers of the Constitution. Locke believed, as did our Founders, that government was established to protect life, liberty, and property. That's the kind of government our Founders sought to create. Protecting these things means having a criminal code. Shouldn't a national government ensure that criminal statutes are uniform throughout the nation?"

"In a unitary system they do," Elaine shot back. "But our system is based on our history back to colonial times, when the feeling was that the residents of a locality knew what was best for their community. And that feeling remains today. Which is why some states are so hard on the use of marijuana and others are not. You lose that in a unitary system. The example I use in my classes is that in France the minister of education can look at the clock and know what every student in the country is studying at that very moment."

"I know that," said Karl abruptly. "I'm not saying that we should go to a unitary system. But Canada has a strong federal system in which all criminal codes are adopted at the national level. What constitutes a crime does not differ based on where in Canada you happen to be standing. I want to do the same thing here. What, constitutionally, prevents that?"

"The Tenth Amendment and the Constitution itself," retorted Elaine. "The Tenth Amendment reserves power to the states, and the Constitution limits what the national government can do. Article III, Section 2, of the Constitution delineates the jurisdiction of the federal court system.

In order to change to a system like Canada's you would need a constitutional amendment, and I doubt it would even pass Congress, let alone get the approval of the necessary thirty-eight states."

"I disagree," replied Karl. "I don't think the Constitution needs to be amended. I think we need to get back to the Founders' original intentions. The Founders felt the main function of government was the protection of property. With the interstate commerce clause and the national supremacy clause I think we can have a national uniform criminal code without amending the Constitution. And as far as Article III, Section 2, goes, that section explains cases under federal jurisdiction, I grant you that. But it does *not* have any language, at least in my view, that excludes taking cases in addition to those specified in that section. What I'm saying is it is open to interpretation. For a long time civil rights were considered a matter solely for the state courts. Then we grew as a nation and reinterpreted the Constitution. Today civil rights are considered federal court issues. I don't see why we can't do the same with crime."

"I don't see your logic," said Elaine, shaking her head.

"Any crime affects commerce," said Karl patiently. "If you trespass on my property, you are affecting its value, which affects commerce. If you kill me, I can no longer buy things. If you rape me, I need medical care and lose time from work, both of which affect commerce. All commerce is interstate commerce these days, so therefore all crime should be covered by the national government. At least that was the logic used when passing the Civil Rights Act, and I don't see any difference with crime."

"Assuming you're right, which I don't necessarily concede," said Elaine, "I see two other problems. First of all, I can't see Congress having the time to develop an all-encompassing criminal code while still trying to perform its other duties, and second, you would lose the local input from the diverse regions of the country. I don't see it working, and I'm not convinced it is in the country's best interest."

"Actually," said Karl thoughtfully, "those are rather weak arguments compared to your earlier ones. Compiling such a code would not be difficult. We already have a large body of federal law and the Uniform Code of Military Justice. Combined, these cover almost every crime. I doubt it would be difficult to integrate them and remove the military language. I can't see any state or local governments arguing that murder, rape, burglary, or child abuse shouldn't be against the law." The professor nodded thoughtfully in agreement.

Karl continued. "The judiciary committees in the House and the Senate could work that out. When it comes to things like prostitution or those states like mine that don't take such a hard line on drugs, the local viewpoints are still represented. The members of Congress are elected at the local and state level. We are there to represent the interests of our communities. I can argue for lax laws on marijuana, and if I can convince enough members to agree with me, the laws regarding marijuana will be changed nationally. Likewise, the members from Nevada can present their case for legalized prostitution. We already represent local concerns on other matters, and our constituents are generally pleased with the results. I don't see why this process wouldn't work just as well with criminal issues.

"Obviously, we wouldn't take everything from the Uniform Code of Military Justice—adultery as a crime just wouldn't work nationally. This would also eliminate the need for the UCMJ; the military would be under the same laws as the rest of the country."

"But," interrupted Elaine, "you would have too many fingers in the pie. Interest groups, members of Congress, everyone trying to get their pet project in. You know how Congress works."

"I know," said Karl. "Which is why I'm saying have the judiciary committees do this. They can work with the American Bar Association and judges' groups to ensure that we're not including too many needless laws. Think of the media. They would have a field day with this. If Representative John Doe from Anywhere, America, tries to insert a law against needle exchange, the media would be all over it. The media scrutiny will help keep the dumb stuff out. This would also get some absurd laws off the books, obsolete laws that are not currently being enforced. For example, in some places it is still legal to beat your wife, if you do it on a Sunday morning in front of City Hall with a stick no wider than your thumb. People are not doing this today, but if some guy wanted to in

that community, legally he could. We need to revamp our entire system."
Elaine just shook her head. Karl went on.

"As to whether or not this would be in the best interest of the country, I
strongly argue that it would. From our earliest beginnings, we have struggled between our identity as a nation and our perception of ourselves as
a collection of communities, our notion of federalism and states' rights.
We even fought a civil war over this issue. Today, 150 years after the Civil
War, we still have problems with states or local governments arguing that
they don't have to comply with federal law; just look at the way some local governments acted when the Patriot Act was passed. With over 87,000
governments in this country, there is very little holding us together. A
uniform national criminal code would help give us an identity; it would
show all Americans that there are standards and values that we all hold
in common. Essentially the only thing holding us together now is our
history. We have very few shared values. The way people think, view our
country, view the government, the culture, are all very different in various parts of the nation. Now, in one sense, that is a strength. But it is also
a weakness. The militia groups and other separatist groups in parts of the
country have such a perverted sense of what it means to be an American
that they're on the verge of starting a civil war. We need something nationally to hold us together.

"It would also help solve some problems. There would be fewer court
fights about jurisdiction or competing claims between federal and state
courts over who has the right to try criminals. Given how congested our
court system is, that reform would definitely be in the best interest of
our country."

"So you would just eliminate all state and local court systems?" asked
Elaine sardonically.

"Not eliminate them, no," replied Karl. "The Sixth Amendment requires that trials be held in the district where the crime was committed.
We would still need state and local courts. But they would be applying
the same law, the national law. They would continue to function as they
do, but they would be part of the federal court system. States would also
have their own court system for divorces, civil suits, and the like. And

these courts could still appeal to the federal courts and raise issues of constitutional importance. But this would eliminate the person in California going to death row while the person in Vermont goes to the penitentiary for life."

"And what about sentencing?" asked Elaine reprovingly. "Would Congress also implement sentencing guidelines for all crimes? As they have with so many federal crimes? You know what a problem that has turned out to be."

"I know there are problems with sentencing guidelines," said Karl with a grimace. "But the idea is fundamentally sound. Yes, there would be guidelines. And I would eliminate plea bargaining. That way you wouldn't have situations like we have today, where the drug runner gets caught and has no one to turn in, but everyone above him turns state's evidence and gets a lesser sentence due to a plea."

"Wouldn't that actually clog up the court system even more than it already is?" asked Elaine. "Think of all those criminals demanding trials."

"Actually, no," said Karl with a smile. "A county in the state of Washington actually abolished plea bargains. Instead of clogging up the system, it actually streamlined it. People who were obviously guilty, who would have previously turned state's evidence, now couldn't get a plea bargain, and they pleaded guilty, hoping for leniency from the judge. I think it would work the same way with my system. That is the laboratories-of-democracy idea at work. Something that worked at the lower level should be taken up nationally. I would want to see a provision for experimental sentencing or punishments in the national guidelines."

"What about the police?" asked Elaine. "If you're going to nationalize the criminal justice system, the courts, and the legal code, shouldn't you also nationalize the police? Or will they stay under local jurisdiction?"

"I hadn't thought about that," admitted Karl. "Logically it makes sense to nationalize them also, to keep everything uniform. But at an instinctive level, I don't think that should be done. Localities have better knowledge of their own requirements for manpower, and it is better if the cops come from the area they'll be responsible for. They know the people and the geography, they develop their own snitches. Maybe, down the line, eventually they should also come under national control, but I don't want it to be everything all at once. That would be too drastic a change. Right now I'd just like to concentrate on the laws all being the same.

"A national criminal justice system might also make some people think twice about committing a crime. For example, let's say I decide to kill my wife. Rather than kill her at our home in New York, where if I get caught I face the death penalty, I wait until we take our summer vacation in Vermont, where if I get caught I only face life in prison. With a national system of laws, I'll think twice about killing my wife. This would also speed things up by standardizing the system. There would only be one definition of a speedy trial—right now that varies from state to state. Different states have different standards about admissible evidence. Some states have reciprocal discovery, where the defense has to turn over information to the prosecution; other states don't have this. Jury selection and instructions would be uniform. And this would allow us to get some bad judges off the state benches, like that idiot who overturned a jury's guilty verdict, saying a woman wasn't raped because it was impossible for the rapist to hold a gun to her head and put a condom on at the same time. The state judges would try civil cases, and that way we could find out if they know what they're doing so the feds could appoint only qualified people to the criminal courts. I mean, if there's an incompetent judge in the civil court, somebody's divorce gets screwed up or something. That's bad, but an incompetent judge in a criminal court sets a murderer free. My system would eliminate that. It would be good for the country."

"Yes," Elaine replied, "and there would only be one bar exam, and attorneys would find it easier to move around the country to practice. You could still have state bar exams for those who are not doing criminal work. But, and you won't like this, as far as I'm concerned, a national criminal justice system is a bad idea. Whenever the feds take over something, they screw it up. You know yourself, too many people want to grab some glory by getting their pet ideas in, a huge bureaucracy is created, and pretty soon all we have is a mess. Realistically, there were sound reasons why welfare was returned to the states. The federal government spent over $400 billion to eradicate poverty over forty years, and the result was an exponential increase in the number of people living in poverty. I realize that there were also other factors, but even you can't argue that federal control of welfare was a success. We need the states as a check and balance on the feds. And you need to think particularly about the state courts checking federal courts. For example, if your system had been in place forty years ago, *Roe v. Wade* could never have taken place. Abortion was illegal in most states then, so in your system it probably would have been illegal nationally. I can't see a federal judge ruling a law like that unconstitutional, which is what a state judge did. We would lose that protection in your system. And when it comes to incarcerating people, this is something so fundamental that I doubt many Americans would be comfortable with the feds assuming this power."

"And that was the same argument the states used when it came to civil rights. They claimed that chaos would result, that the feds would screw everything up. Forty years later, I think you would agree we did a pretty good job on that," snapped Karl. "Also, keep in mind that federal judges routinely find acts of Congress unconstitutional. They could do the same with some of the laws in the uniform criminal code."

"True, to some extent," granted Elaine. "But this is different. I know in the 1950s and 1960s we had the Klan and other supremacist groups, but today we have so many militia groups, armed and angry, claiming that the feds have taken away too many of their rights. I can't see them sitting back and letting this happen. It might set off another Civil War."

"Actually," Karl said thoughtfully, "it might give us a chance to clarify the Second Amendment and disarm the militias. You and I both know that the Founders intended the Second Amendment to mean state-sponsored militias, not private ones like those cropping up now."

"If federal appeals courts can't even agree on that, I doubt Congress could," sighed Elaine. "And I doubt a uniform criminal code could be used to disarm the militias. They would become even more radical, trying to defend their rights from the federal government's unwarranted intrusion. Your idea might actually precipitate a crisis."

"I don't think so," said Karl stubbornly. "I think the vast majority of Americans are law-abiding people and will comply with the government once the issue is resolved. The fact that there is so much confusion about it gives the militias a leg to stand on. If we eliminate that confusion, they will abide by the law. And we could enact meaningful gun control laws to ban some guns and ammunition nationally. Some states have already enacted such bans, but people just go to neighboring states to buy what they want. I grant you there will always be a black market, but with national laws and national sentencing guidelines, you wouldn't have cases like the ones in Texas, where a valid defense is 'he needed killin'.'"

Elaine said, "But don't you see, that is part of the problem. The cops and juries will still be local, have the local mentality. Juries in Texas may not actually hear the 'he needed killin'' defense, because your judge wouldn't allow it, but in their minds they will be thinking it and that will affect their decision. And giving this country a uniform criminal code will not change the mentality of the cops. They will still decide which crimes to give priority; they will still ignore some crimes and focus on crimes they see as more important. Nothing you've proposed is going to make the cops devote the same resources to the murder of a little brown girl as they devote to the murder of a little white girl. There is a basic inequity in the fact that laws vary from locality to locality, but in my mind the greater problem is the racism in the system. Your changes will do nothing about that." She looked at Karl.

"You're right, of course," he smiled as he replied. "We can't fix everything at once. What we can do is try to fix what can be fixed. And, as a result of the Civil Rights Act, attitudes about race in this country have changed. It is possible the same thing could happen with crime. We would begin thinking about crime and ourselves in a new way, and forty years from now the racism in the system would be much less of a problem. Basically, we need to eliminate some of the glaring disparities in our country, many of which affect people of color. Depriving someone of their freedom, convicting them of a crime, is so fundamental that I think we need a national criminal code. Can I count on your support?" asked Karl.

Elaine sat quietly, mulling over Karl's arguments. He had made some valid points. Could we really claim to be a nation where everyone was equal if the definition of criminal behavior differed so greatly through-out the country? Could we really call ourselves a nation when there was so little holding the disparate communities together? These were good points. But the states had existed long before the national government and were a definite protector of rights. The struggle between the national government and the states was an inherent part of our government and culture. Wouldn't a national criminal code essentially kill federalism? "I need to give this some thought," Elaine told Karl. "I'll let you know what I decide."

Points to Ponder

Agree or disagree with the following statements, and give your reasons:

1. It is fundamentally wrong that what is considered a crime in one state is not a crime in another.

2. The states are not "laboratories of democracy" because good ideas like needle exchange or legalized prostitution rarely go national.

3. We need a better way to achieve national standards for defining crimes or rights, rather than waiting for the Supreme Court to rule.

4. A uniform national criminal code would help hold this nation of diverse states together.

5. Elaine is right: whenever the federal government gets involved in something, they screw it up.

6. The state court systems provide a necessary check on the federal government.

7. The original colonists were right: local residents know what is best for their community. Rather than expanding the role of the federal government, as Karl suggests, it needs to be dramatically reduced, giving more power back to the states and localities.

8. Although there are problems with sentencing guidelines, overall they are a good idea. They prevent judges from abusing their power.

9. Eliminating plea bargaining would be in the best interest of justice.

10. Karl is wrong: nothing will appease the militias.

11. Karl's system will eventually change attitudes enough that racism will no longer be endemic to our judicial system.

12. Elaine is right: the cops and the juries will ensure that, even if Karl's plan is adopted, nothing will really change.

13. Karl is right: there is really nothing but history holding this nation together. We need something more.

14. The great strength of this country is the diversity of local communities; this is where many of the greatest innovations in our country have come from.

15. If you were Elaine, would you support Karl's program?

Essay Questions

1. Discuss the advantages and disadvantages of our federalist system. What are the problems? Do you think the benefits outweigh the problems? Why? What changes would you make to the system?

2. Although we have a nation, it is a nation of states. In spite of what Karl says, there are many things holding this country together. Discuss these things and whether or not you feel they are enough to hold together fifty disparate states. What changes would you make, if any?

Chapter 3

Whose Privacy? Whose Rights?:
Civil Liberties

Linda looked at the stick, crying. There was no mistake; this was the third pregnancy test. All said the same thing: She was pregnant. She was sixteen years old, a junior in high school, and pregnant. What was she going to do? There was only one bright spot—Dad was on a business trip. He would be gone for two weeks. Maybe she and Mom could find a solution before Dad came home and blew his stack. Linda washed her face and went out into the living room.

"Linda, honey, what's wrong?" Mrs. Moore asked, seeing her daughter's red eyes.

"Mom, please, don't yell, okay? It's bad, but I need to talk. Please just listen, okay?"

Mrs. Moore nodded mutely, dreading not knowing, yet afraid to find out what was wrong with her daughter.

Linda took a deep breath. "You remember last month, when the volleyball team got to go to the matches in Hawaii?"

Mrs. Moore nodded, and Linda continued. "Well, you know how Coach Mark has always been so helpful to me, encouraging me . . . He was worried that I might have hurt my ankle during the first game of the tournament. He brought an ice pack up to my room, and . . . and well, . . . I'm pregnant."

Mrs. Moore gripped the arms of her chair, her knuckles turning white. "Linda, are you saying you and the coach . . . "

"Yes, Mom, we made love. I was a virgin, and he told me I couldn't get pregnant the first time. But he had rubbers and used them anyway. I just don't understand how this happened. And I don't know what to do now. . . ."

Mrs. Moore wiped her tears away. "Okay, Linda, let's start from the beginning. What about your roommate—where was she during all this?"

Linda shook her head. "I didn't have a roommate at first. Trish was sick, so she joined the team later in the week. The coach made the room assignments, and I had my own room for three days."

"And the coach slept with you?"

"Yes. Not the first night, but the second and third."

"So you're one month pregnant. What do you want to do?" Mrs. Moore asked, while thinking, I will kill him. I will string him up by his balls and then set him on fire. And that will be nothing compared to what Joe would do . . .

Linda began to cry again. "Oh, Mom. I can't have a baby now. You know I've already had scouts from several colleges show interest in me. Stanford is talking about a full athletic scholarship. But if I have this baby I won't be able to play softball this year and might even miss volleyball next year. There is no way I can get a scholarship then. I know it sounds selfish. It *is* selfish. But what kind of mother could I be if I don't go to college? What kind of job could I get to support the baby and myself? You and Dad can't help—we're barely surviving as it is."

"I know, Linda. But it's almost never the right time to have a baby. I was barely out of high school myself when you were born." Mrs. Moore was still entertaining fantasies of killing the coach, but she was surprised at how mature her daughter sounded.

"Yes, and you've often said how sorry you were that you didn't wait longer to start a family," Linda retorted.

"Linda, as you get older, you'll find that we all have regrets. Yes, I would have liked to go to college and have a career. I think I could have been a better mother if I had been older when you were born. But I've never regretted having you." Mrs. Moore smiled at her daughter through her tears.

"I don't know what to do, Mom. I want to go to college. You know how long I've been planning on being a lawyer. But if I have this baby, even if I put it up for adoption, I might not get those scholarships. But I don't know if I could have an abortion. I don't know if I could kill this child growing inside me." Linda began crying again.

"Well, honey . . . ," Mrs. Moore's voice trailed off as she heard the front door closing.

"Betty, Linda, I'm home. The trip was cut short. Where are you?" Linda ran to her bedroom and shut the door before her father could see her and ask why she was upset. Betty Moore composed her face before calling out to her husband, "I'm in here, Joe. Why was the trip cut short?"

"Oh, honey, it's bad. The new line is defective. Management just found out. They have to redesign it. I've been laid off for at least six months. I'll be able to get unemployment insurance, but I don't know how we'll meet all the bills. Even with your paycheck, we just won't have enough. Honey, Betty, it's not that bad. We've had tough times before. Please don't cry." Joe held his wife. Through her tears she told her husband about Linda's problem. Suddenly being laid off was not the catastrophe Joe had thought. Joe hugged his wife, then went to his daughter.

"Okay, Linda, Princess, let me see if I have this right. Your volleyball coach came into your room in Hawaii, slept with you two nights in a row, got you pregnant, and you don't know what to do. Is that about it?" Joe kept his voice level, gentle even, although his body trembled with rage.

Linda nodded, afraid to say anything for fear of triggering her father's temper. She just couldn't deal with his yelling right now.

"Well, Princess, I'll tell you what we're going to do. First we're going to call the police and file charges against Coach Mark Bramwell. Then tomorrow we'll take you to the clinic for an abortion. You will not have your life ruined because that coach couldn't keep his pants zipped." Joe Moore knew that the longer his daughter was pregnant, the more difficult it would be for her to decide to abort the child. He had seen his wife in the same situation seventeen years earlier; he'd begged Betty to either get an abortion or put the child up for adoption. Betty had refused and they married. Although Joe loved his wife and daughter, he wanted better for Linda.

"No, Daddy, you can't!" exclaimed Linda. "If we go to the police, everyone will know. No college will take me then. At least not on scholarship."

"Linda, honey, you're a minor. No one will know your name," Joe tried to reassure his daughter.

"Really, Daddy? Do you think the other members of the team don't know I was the only one without a roommate? They'll know, and the college scouts will find out. Besides, I don't know if I want an abortion!" Linda cried, looking to her mother, who had just come into her room, for support.

"Hush, Princess," Joe grimaced. "Well, we can talk about what to do about the coach. But you have to decide: do you want to go to college and be a lawyer or do you want life as a single mother? Keep in mind, you won't be able to stay in high school if you're pregnant. In this state they don't allow that; you would have to go to the school established for pregnant girls. And the coach is married already, so it's not like he can marry you and raise the child."

"I know you're right, Daddy. I know I have to have an abortion. It's the only choice. But I won't let you call the police." Joe looked at his daughter and, recognizing the determined set of her chin, nodded. She would not give in, he knew from experience with that look.

"Joe . . . ," Betty said tentatively, "why don't we just tell the principal?"

Joe nodded approvingly. "Princess, what do you think? The coach will lose his job, but the principal will keep it quiet about you. He won't want the school board to know what kind of a man he hired."

Linda nodded slowly, "I guess so."

Joe went to call the principal before his daughter could change her mind.

★   ★   ★

"What did the principal want, Mark? Why did he call you in on a Sunday?" Krissy Bramwell looked at her husband with concern.

Mark stared at the kitchen table, head in his hands. "I've been fired," he choked out.

"Fired? Why? You're a great coach and everyone knows it. You have a contract. What grounds did he give for firing you? We can get some of the other lawyers at the firm to fight this." Krissy knew that schools all over the country had offered her husband contracts.

Mark glanced at Krissy. "He, um, says that I violated my contract. There's a . . . morals clause and I violated it . . . um . . . by sleeping with one of my students." Mark was talking to the table, unable to meet his wife's eyes.

"That little slut!" exploded Krissy. "She told, didn't she? It's not enough she seduces you and tries to ruin our marriage, she wants to get you fired for not continuing the affair. How dare she!" Krissy was furious. The affair still hurt, but she loved her husband.

"It's not like that," Mark gulped, again refusing to meet his wife's eyes. "She's pregnant. Her parents decided to protect her privacy by not going to the police. The principal agreed to keep it quiet, but Linda's father insisted I be fired."

"Pregnant?" whispered Krissy. "She's going to have a baby and blamed it on you? It probably isn't even yours." Krissy thought about all of the visits to the fertility clinic, the expense of attempting to get pregnant, the numerous times they had forced themselves to make love because it was "the optimal time" for her to get pregnant, the visits to the infertility specialists, the expense of the treatments—all that, and no child.

"It is." Mark's voice was steadier now. Krissy was taking this better than he had thought she would. "She was a virgin. And she's so focused on her schoolwork and sports that she rarely even talks to the guys at school. I'm not defending her, but she's not a slut. It is my baby."

"She's going to have your baby," Krissy repeated, hurt in her eyes, meanwhile thinking, It's not fair. I put off having kids to get my career started, and now I can't have kids. She doesn't want a kid, but she's pregnant. It just isn't fair.

"Well, no . . . ," Mark replied. "She's going to have an abortion. At least, according to the principal, that is what she and her family have decided."

"Abort your child? We'll see about that," said Krissy. "This is what we're going to do." After she explained her plan to Mark, he agreed with what she proposed. Krissy went to the phone and began making some calls.

★   ★   ★

"How was school, Linda?" Betty Moore asked her daughter at the dinner table the next night.

"Everyone was talking about the coach, wondering why he had been fired. It was hard." Linda blinked back tears.

"Oh, Princess," Joe said to his daughter, "I called the clinic. They can do the abortion on Friday. You'll have to miss school that day, but one day won't be that much. Then you can focus on your studies." Just then the doorbell rang. "Who could that be?" Joe wondered.

"Linda, it's for you," Betty called from the front door.

Linda went to the door, but she didn't recognize the woman standing there.

"Linda Moore?" the woman asked. Linda nodded her head, curious. The woman handed her a piece of paper and said, "You've been served." She then turned and left.

Linda looked at the woman walking away and then at the paper in her hand, confused. By now Joe had joined his wife and daughter at the door. He took the piece of paper, read it, and said, "Oh, God."

"What is it, Joe?" asked Betty. Joe just shook his head.

★   ★   ★

Six weeks later: "All rise," intoned the bailiff. "This court is now in session. The honorable Rita Smith presiding. Be seated."

Judge Smith cleared her throat. "In the case of Bramwell v. Linda M, are all parties present and represented by counsel?" She looked out at the courtroom, struck by the similar looks of Linda and Mrs. Bramwell. Both women were thin, blond with blue eyes, and tall. They almost looked like sisters.

"Yes, Your Honor," they replied.

"Very good," stated the judge. "I recognize William Salvos for the plaintiffs, but I do not know the other counsel."

"Amy Mathers, Your Honor, from Women for Choice, representing Ms. M," replied one attorney.

"John Tracy, Your Honor, from Citizens for Life, representing the fetus," said the other attorney.

"Very well. The appearances are entered into the record. As there is a minor child involved, I am reminding counsel and the media that the defendant will be referred to as Linda M. to protect her identity. Does everyone understand?" Judge Smith looked out at a chorus of nodding heads. "I have read the petitions submitted by all parties and have familiarized myself with the citations. Proceed, Mr. Salvos."

"Your Honor, my client seeks an extension of the emergency Temporary Restraining Order prohibiting Ms. M from obtaining an abortion. She is pregnant with my client's child. We request the court to bar her from aborting that child. My client and his wife would then seek custody of the child to raise as their own." Mr. Salvos was ready to continue his argument, but the judge interrupted him.

"Mr. Salvos, let me make sure I have the facts right. Your married client ignored his marriage vows, had an affair with a minor female, who was under his care at the time, who is under the age of consent . . . " Rita stopped and looked at Mr. Salvos, who nodded that her summary was correct. She then continued, "You want me to ignore *Roe v. Wade* and force this young woman to bear a child against her will so that your client and his wife can raise the child?" Judge Smith was incredulous.

"Essentially, Your Honor," replied William Salvos, "that is correct. My client is aware that he was wrong to take advantage of his authority over Ms. M. However, he feels that the wrong would be compounded by allowing Ms. M to abort the child. Mr. Bramwell and his wife want children. Unfortunately, Mrs. Bramwell is unable to bear children. This would prevent the psychological harm to Ms. M of having an abortion and allow the Bramwells to have a child. My clients also have religious objections to abortion; they feel that it is wrong to terminate a pregnancy."

"Your Honor!" Amy Mathers jumped up.

"Sit down, Ms. Mathers. You will get your chance when I've finished with Mr. Salvos." Amy sank back to her chair under the judge's glare. Judge Smith then turned her glare on Mr. Salvos. "Tell me, Mr. Salvos, why shouldn't I order my bailiff to take Mr. Bramwell into custody so that he can be charged with statutory rape? After all, Ms. M is not yet of the age of consent in this state."

"True, Your Honor," conceded Mr. Salvos. "However, Ms. M is old enough to consent to sex in Hawaii, which is where the child was conceived. And both parties agree that the sex only took place in Hawaii."

"I see. And tell me, Mr. Salvos, what religion your clients practice. I would be interested to know of a religion that approves of premarital or extramarital sex but does not approve of abortion," the judge said with ice in her voice.

"My clients are Christians, Your Honor. And no, their church does not approve of extramarital affairs. However, allowing the abortion would simply compound the sin," Mr. Salvos replied sheepishly, knowing that this part of the argument was not strong.

"Sit down, Mr. Salvos," ordered the judge. "Ms. Mathers, what do you have to say?"

Amy Mathers smirked at Salvos and, standing, addressed the judge. "Your Honor, I'm not sure the fact that the sex took place in Hawaii exonerates Mr. Bramwell from criminal charges. It is not legal to transport a minor across state lines for immoral purposes. The ostensible reason for the trip to Hawaii was a volleyball tournament, but given what we've heard here and the facts that we have about how this child was conceived, I don't think we can discount Mr. Bramwell's motives. There is also the fact of the striking similarity in the looks of my client and Mrs. Bramwell. It is almost as if Mr. Bramwell chose to have an affair with someone who resembled his wife. While I'm not making any accusations at this point, it did strike me that he might have had sex with Ms. M simply because any child that might result could be passed off as his wife's child." The judge nodded her head slowly, while Mr. Salvos shook his head grimly, ignoring his clients' attempts to have him raise an objection. Amy continued, "However, the fact remains that my client has a constitutional right to an abortion. Even though parental consent is not necessary in this state, she has the support of both her parents. Mr. Bramwell seeks to benefit from his immoral and possibly illegal act. To allow him to do so is wrong. To force my client to bear this child would subject her to significant health risks and would also impact her education detrimentally." Amy sat down.

"Your Honor!" Judge Smith nodded at Mr. Salvos. "I object to Ms. Mathers's characterization. Ms. M is a healthy young woman. Carrying this baby to term does not subject her to 'significant health risks.' It would inconvenience her, but she is old enough to know that there are consequences for her actions. In addition, although I do not concede that Mr. Bramwell's actions were illegal, courts in this state have ruled that illegal actions do not negate parental rights. Last month Judge Jordan ruled that Wilbur Smythe, convicted of raping Eleanor K, has visitation rights to the child that was conceived during that rape. Mr. Bramwell, I repeat, did not commit rape, but the point is that even if the child was conceived in an illegal manner, the father does have rights regarding that child." Mr. Salvos sat down, and Judge Smith turned to Ms. Mathers, eyebrows raised.

Ms. Mathers replied, "Your Honor, any pregnancy presents risks of diabetes, thyroid problems, and high blood pressure, to name just a few potential health risks. With a teenager there are more risks, and, if necessary, we can call witnesses to address this point. In the *Smythe* case, Eleanor K decided, of her own free will, to carry that child to term. While I disagree with Judge Jordan's decision allowing visitation rights to Smythe, Ms. K made the decision to bear the child. That is not the case here. The bottom line is that *Roe* is the law of the land. A woman has the right to decide on an abortion in the first trimester, and the father has no say. You must void this temporary restraining order and let Ms. M get on with her life."

"Any last words, Mr. Salvos?" asked the judge.

"It is time to give fathers some rights in this matter. One of Ms. M's main concerns is the potential loss of scholarships if she continues this pregnancy. My clients have offered to establish a trust fund for her education. This would enable Ms. M to continue her life without killing my client's unborn child. This would also prevent the psychological trauma of an abortion, allow my client to raise his child, and allow Ms. M to do the right thing. Your Honor, you can take a stand in this courtroom to equalize the law, giving men reproductive rights, and help reduce the genocide that abortion has brought to this country." Salvos sat down.

"Tell me, Counselor," asked the judge, "if you want fathers to have rights in terms of reproduction, are you willing to support full paternal rights? If Linda M wanted to keep this child, would you argue that she needs the father's consent to keep the child? In your world, would the father be able to demand an abortion?"

"Your Honor," replied Salvos, "fathers in this country have no rights until the woman makes a decision to have or to abort the child. So yes, I would argue that a man can request an abortion when the woman wants to keep the child. I don't think I want to go to the extreme of arguing that a father can force a mother to abort a child against her will, but I do think that the father can demonstrate to a court that he had no desire to become a parent and waive all parental rights."

The judge shook her head, looked at Ms. Mathers, and asked, "Any final thoughts, Counselor?"

"Yes, Your Honor." Ms. Mathers stood up. "Essentially what Mr. Salvos and his clients are asking for is to turn Ms. M into a type of prostitute. If they didn't have the money to set up a trust fund, would they still have rights to her child? Is this a new version of rent-a-womb? Women have the right in this country to control their own bodies. How would this be any different from selling her child? Also, if the Bramwells want a child that desperately, they can have one themselves. There is no need for my client to bear a child for them. The Bramwells can find a woman to carry an egg fertilized by his sperm, which is what they are requesting here, but Ms. M does not wish to volunteer to do this. What the Bramwells are requesting is abhorrent."

"You make some valid points," smiled the judge. "Mr. Salvos, while there is some validity to the point that men have no rights when it comes to questions of reproduction, you must also keep in mind that men do have rights here—they have the right not to have sex, and they also have the right to practice birth control. If your client does not like the fact that women in this country have rights that men do not, then he should simply not have unprotected sex."

Attorney Salvos grimaced. "You're right, Your Honor. Men need to learn to take responsibility for birth control. Unfortunately, too many men still feel it is the woman's responsibility. However, the fact remains that in this case you can bring some good out of this situation. Allow Mr. and Mrs. Bramwell to raise this child."

The judge responded with a series of questions. "What happens if I do prevent this abortion and Linda decides to keep the child? Would you have me turn pregnant girls into incubators? Would I be seeing you and Ms. Mathers in this courtroom arguing over who is better fit to be a parent? Would you be arguing that in spite of the fact that Mr. Bramwell violated his marriage vows, he and his wife would make better parents than Ms. M? You are seeking to punish Ms. M because Mrs. Bramwell put off bearing children until it was too late. If Mrs. Bramwell were to find herself pregnant today, would you be arguing this case? Isn't it simply that your clients want a child, not that they have such strong objections to abortion? If Ms. M were a crack addict with brown skin, would your clients still want to keep the child? If I give Mr. Bramwell rights in this case, won't I be denying the rights of the mother? Why should I put Mr. Bramwell's rights above Ms. M's?"

"Because, Your Honor," replied Mr. Salvos, "by giving Linda M the rights, you are denying any rights to Mr. Bramwell. If we are going to deny rights to one party, shouldn't we side with life? Why should we side with abortion? As far as I'm concerned, I would love to be back here in six months arguing which party would be the better custodial parent. As for your other questions, I don't know. I do know that the situation we are dealing with is not as complicated as you make out. I see no reason to address those issues here."

"Mr. Salvos, you know as well as I do that, if I give you your TRO, at a later date a judge in this state will be facing those questions I asked. Can Mr. and Mrs. Bramwell state under oath that their convictions are so strong that they would be requesting a TRO if Ms. M were a brown-skinned crack addict? Well?" asked the judge.

Mark and Krissy Bramwell looked aghast. This was not going as they had planned.

"Your Honor, with all due respect . . . "

"Mr. Salvos, you and I both know that when an attorney starts out an argument with that phrase, there is no respect at all," interjected the judge.

"Your Honor," Mr. Salvos began again, "I apologize. There was no disrespect intended. However, it is my understanding that the courts in this country do not deal with hypothetical situations. We must deal with the situation that we have here. Ms. M is pregnant, and my clients want to raise the child. There is no reasonable argument to be made that the mother's rights outweigh those of the father."

"Mr. Salvos," said the judge acerbically, "women are the ones who carry the children. When men can carry the fetus, then they will be able to make all of the decisions. Now, Mr. Tracy, what are you doing here, and what do you have to contribute to this discussion?"

"Your Honor," began the attorney, "as I said, I'm here representing the fetus. First of all, I would like to renew my objection to the gag order. There is no reason to withhold Ms. M's full name. What she wants to do is kill her unborn child. The public has a right to know that. This decision affects the community. They have a right to know this, to attempt to reason with her. I know that this child was conceived as a result of statutory rape. In my mind, we should no longer keep the names of rape victims private; it just perpetuates the myth that the woman is somehow responsible for the crime. As long as victims' names are withheld, this problem will continue. It is also a matter of equality. Mr. Bramwell's name has been publicized. He is feeling community pressure because of his actions. As a general principle, I find it offensive that a man can publicly be labeled a rapist before trial, but his accuser retains her anonymity. Given how the media publicizes accusations of rape against high-profile men, I feel it is only equitable that the woman's name be publicized also."

"Mr. Tracy, your position is laudable, but that is not the issue here. While I agree that women should not be seen as responsible for rape and I applaud the victims who allow their names to be published, given the circumstances here I will not change my ruling. And it seems to me that your primary objective here is not to change the way this country views rape and rape victims, but rather to openly name Ms. M so that pro-life activists can put pressure on her. While I understand that everyone has a right to freedom of speech and that the media has rights, I will not change my mind. Please speak to the issue at hand, the TRO preventing Ms. M from obtaining an abortion," the judge said harshly.

"Very well, Your Honor. My organization is pro-life, and we would like to speak to the rights of the unborn child in this case. As you know, several judges in this state as well as other states have incarcerated pregnant women who were on drugs, citing the rights of the unborn child. In my mind, that establishes the fact that the fetus has rights. Shouldn't we protect the fetus's right to live in this case?"

"Mr. Tracy," replied the judge, "I am not going to get into that argument. That is something for the Supreme Court to address. As it is, the law says that the fetus lives at the discretion of the mother in the first trimester. That is the case here. While I would agree that a fetus at seven or eight months has rights, the Supreme Court has ruled otherwise in the first trimester. I am not willing to engage in a discussion of the rights of the fetus."

"But Your Honor," continued Mr. Tracy, "shouldn't we engage in that discussion? As you know, the Supreme Court has been wrong in the past. Maybe we need to start the change here. Why is it appropriate to give the unborn child rights at seven months of gestation and not at three months? Isn't it just as alive at that time? You must remember, that since *Roe* more than forty million abortions have been performed in this country. We are committing mass murder. You need to take a stand here and now, and say that it is wrong. We must speak for the unborn. We must also think about the equal protection clause of the Fourteenth Amendment. Doesn't the father deserve equal protection of the laws? Doesn't the fetus deserve that same protection?"

The judge simply looked at Mr. Tracy and shook her head. "Mr. Tracy, it is not within my ability, even if I so choose, to overturn the Supreme Court. *Roe* is the law of the land. *Roe* does not give a first-trimester fetus rights. Please, if you don't have any cases on point, sit down."

In the gallery, an old woman was crying, looking at her granddaughter. Mrs. Cooke, Betty's mother, sat watching her granddaughter's struggle while remembering her own experience of fifty years earlier. We just weren't ready for another child, she thought. Bob was out of work, and I couldn't even find enough money for food for the two we already had. Thank God Bob never found out. It was painful and scary with the knitting needle, but I survived. And I was still able to get pregnant later. Otherwise I never would have had Betty. Don't let this judge put my Linda through what I went through. The best thing that came from legalized abortion is the fact that women no longer have to do what I did to survive.

"There is something else, Your Honor," Mr. Tracy interjected. The judge glared at him. "There is a compromise available that will resolve this situation. That compromise is ectogenesis." Seeing the confused look on the judge's face, he hurriedly continued. "Ectogenesis is the technology of an artificial womb. Scientists began having success with these experiments a few years ago, in 2003. Today they have the ability to take some cells from Ms. M's womb and create an artificial womb. The baby can then be transferred to that artificial womb until gestation is complete. This would allow Ms. M to continue her life without an invasion of her privacy because the operation is similar to an abortion. It would allow the Bramwells to then take the child."

"Your Honor!" exclaimed Ms. Mathers.

"Just a minute, Ms. Mathers," the judge said. "Mr. Tracy, are you telling me this has been done successfully? I don't recall hearing anything in the news."

"No, Your Honor, it has not yet been performed successfully with a human. But since 2003 it has been successful with a number of animal species." Mr. Tracy took a deep breath. "And just recently it was performed successfully with primates. Scientists are now ready to try it on humans. I would argue that this is a perfect case for such a test. I would also argue that *Roe* does not apply if we look at ectogenesis. *Roe* gave women the right to control their own bodies, not the right to control their own reproduction."

The judge shook her head. "Ms. Mathers?"

"Your Honor, I have not had an opportunity to discuss this with my client, but it strikes me as offensive. Mr. Tracy is wrong: the privacy rights of *Roe* are not only about controlling your own body, they are also about controlling reproduction. Ms. M would have no control here of her reproduction; the child would be born and would probably one day want a relationship with her. Ectogenesis threatens a woman's right to choose whether or not to have a child. I find it too extreme to even discuss."

"Your Honor," said Mr. Salvos, and the judge nodded at him. "I can sympathize with Ms. Mathers, but she has made my point for me. Right now men don't have any control over whether or not a child is born. It would seem to me that ectogenesis is a reasonable compromise that would meet everyone's needs."

Judge Rita Smith looked at the Bramwells and then at the Moores, not knowing what was going through their minds. She thought about the child she had aborted twenty years ago. She still wondered whether that had been the right decision. She thought, Why me? Why couldn't this case have gone before another judge? Aloud she said, "All right, I've heard your arguments and read your briefs. This is an important decision. Since time is of the essence, I will give you my decision tomorrow morning."

Points to Ponder

Agree or disagree with the following statements, and give your reasons:

1. Mark should be charged with statutory rape.

2. Linda is mature, as seen from her discussion with her mother. She is mature enough to consent to have sex.

3. Ectogenesis is a developing science. In what ways might it affect women's rights, the abortion debate, and civil liberties?

4. Mark is not trying to benefit from his wrongdoing, he is trying to make the best of a bad situation.

5. It is wrong that a woman has all the rights in abortion. A woman can make a man a father against his will, but she can also deprive him of fatherhood without his consent. This is not fair.

6. The fact that Mark had an affair shows his marriage is not stable. It would be wrong to put a child into that household.

7. Many women in the right-to-life movement are like Krissy: they've put off having children until their careers are established and then cannot have children. They want these healthy babies born so they can adopt the children.

8. Mr. Tracy is right: it makes no sense to give a seven-month fetus rights and deny them to a three-month fetus. The unborn child should have rights protected by law.

9. The Moores cannot afford the costs associated with this pregnancy. The abortion should be allowed.

10. It is morally offensive that a rapist is allowed visitation rights to the child he fathered during a rape.

11. It is important for a child to know its father. Therefore rapists should be allowed to have parental rights to the child that results from a rape.

12. There is never an acceptable reason for abortion.

13. The age of consent in most states is eighteen. Given how society has changed and how much more mature teenagers are these days, the age of consent should be lowered to sixteen at least.

14. Parental consent laws should be mandatory nationally. Parents have a right to know what happens to their children.

15. Linda's grandmother is right: as long as abortion is legal, women will not self-abort. Therefore, we need to keep abortion on demand legal.

16. Whether they are pro-choice or pro-life, most people agree that we have had too many abortions in this country. What can the government do to decrease the number of abortions and still protect the reproductive rights of women?

17. Mr. Tracy is right: we need to publicize the names of rape victims in this country. We need to do this to get rid of the stigma that is associated with rape, so that it will be seen as no different from any other crime.

18. Mr. Tracy has a point: if we publicize the names of accused rapists, we should publicize the names of their accusers.

19. Ectogenesis provides a reasonable alternative to abortion and should receive support from the government.

20. If you were the judge in this case, how would you rule?

Essay Questions

1. Discuss the problems associated with the right to privacy, using some of the issues here to illustrate your points. Keep in mind, the right to privacy is not only related to abortion but also to the media and "the public's right to know."

2. Discuss the issue of giving rights to accused or convicted criminals. Where should we draw the line?

Chapter 4

When Rights Conflict:
Civil Rights and Disabilities

Hello, Charles, Meredith, Jack, how are you today?" asked Congress-woman Julie Dustman brightly, while privately she wondered what the three wanted.

"Just fine, Congresswoman," replied Charles White jovially. "It's been a while. We haven't really talked since your election. How are you enjoying life in Washington?"

"Well, Charles, I do have to say it is interesting," replied Julie. The comment about her election had put her guard up. Charles was a strong lobbyist. If he mentioned the election, it meant he expected something from her. Now was the time to pay for his support during her campaign. Julie only hoped the price would not be too high. "Life here in Congress is a lot more complicated than I thought it would be."

"Yes, ma'am, we all find that out after we've been here a while," agreed the lobbyist.

"It is nice to see you, Jack. How are you finding life in retirement? Is it everything you expected it to be?" Julie wanted to draw out Jack Delancy. What was the retired firefighter doing here and in company with Mer-edith, an active firefighter? Obviously Jack and Charles had come to an agreement on something and had Meredith's support, but Julie just could not imagine what it was.

"Hello, Congresswoman. Actually, retirement is not all it's cracked up to be. I've gone back to work. I'm now the legislative coordinator for the Firemen's Union. This way I can have greater control over my hours but still be involved with the issues that have influenced my career." Jack smiled at Julie, watching the confusion play out on her face.

"Well, that's nice. It's good that someone who actually has experience as a firefighter is advising the union and legislators . . . " Julie's voice trailed off, as she realized the implications of these people all being in her office at the same time.

"Yes, Congresswoman," smiled Charles White, "we do have an issue that we would like you to address. Jack, Meredith, and I feel that since the Firemen's Union gave you such strong support during your campaign, you would be the appropriate member of Congress to introduce some legislation we feel is necessary."

"I see," responded Julie quietly. "Just what do you have in mind?"

"As you know," began Charles, "the Americans with Disabilities Act is coming up for renewal." Charles noted the confused look in the congresswoman's eyes. "The Firemen's Union, as well as other unions of rescue workers, would like to see the act amended." Jack nodded as Charles finished talking.

"Just what type of amendment were you thinking of?" asked Julie cautiously.

"I'd like to respond to that, Congresswoman," said Jack. "The ADA currently prohibits any discrimination based on physical disability and mandates that businesses be accessible to people with disabilities."

Julie nodded. This was not something new. What could the union want?

Jack continued, "We would like to see that modified. Essentially, if you are not physically able to walk down stairs to exit a building in an emergency, you should not be allowed to work above the fifth floor of any building. Hold on, hear me out." Jack saw that Julie was about to interrupt. She sat back, frowning. "I realize this sounds bad, but you need to understand our reasoning. In an emergency, when a building is on fire or there is a gas leak, the electricity is either cut off or turned off. Now, if there is someone obese, over 400 pounds, on the twentieth floor, it takes at least four rescue personnel to carry that person downstairs. Keep in mind that people who can walk down the stairs do not need any help from rescue personnel. That means we can concentrate on helping the injured, putting out the fire, or finding the gas leak. During the World Trade Center disaster, at least one firefighter stayed with a woman in a wheelchair. The rescue worker died with that woman. Now, he did make that choice. But we are trained to do everything humanly possible to help someone during a rescue situation. We are also trained to go first to the person who needs our help most. In the Las Vegas disaster, three rescue workers died helping disabled people who were trying to get out of the hotel. Those workers were trying to help a grossly overweight man. This man could have simply dieted and exercised; it would have helped save the lives of rescue workers. These kinds of situations are not in the best interest of society."

"Now wait a minute," interrupted Julie. "Rescue personnel voluntarily take their jobs. They know that they will be risking their lives on a regular basis. You are asking the government to dramatically limit the rights of people with disabilities in order to possibly save the lives of people who have voluntarily taken the job to rescue them. I don't see how you can justify this."

"Congresswoman, I know this sounds harsh and we're advocating a radically new interpretation of the rights of the disabled," said Charles, "but we have two competing societal values here. The disabled and obese have rights, but so do rescue workers. They know that they are risking their lives on a regular basis. However, allowing someone with severe disabilities to work on the seventieth floor of the World Trade Center nowadays is just socially irresponsible. It pretty much guarantees that some rescue personnel will die in an emergency evacuation. The disabled don't have the right to put the lives of rescue personnel in jeopardy, or the lives of those who are not disabled but need help from rescue personnel. The disabled can get jobs where they work on the lowest floors of a building, and they can also be assigned those hotel rooms or have their apartments in the lower floors. Some of them, like the grossly overweight man, can actually change their situations so that they are no longer disabled. They have that choice. Rescue personnel do not have the choice of passing by that disabled person on the seventieth floor. That is the essential problem. Well, let me rephrase that. The rescue personnel can pass by that disabled person but run the risk of being sued if they do."

"Are you aware of the fact that I have a niece in a wheelchair?" asked Julie angrily. "You are asking me to dramatically limit her choices in life. I find that difficult to even consider."

"Congresswoman, we do realize that you have a disabled niece. That is why we want you to introduce this bill," replied Jack. "Let me ask you this: can you look me in the eye and say, with a clear heart, that in an emergency, Meredith and I should focus on getting your niece out of the building instead of helping you and ten other people climb over the debris to get out of the building? Not only would Meredith and I likely die, but many people without disabilities have a much less chance of surviving if we are concentrating on your niece."

"I find this entire conversation offensive. How could you even approach me with a question like that?" asked Julie in angry astonishment.

"Unfortunately, Congresswoman," replied Jack somberly, "that is a question rescue workers have to ask themselves on a fairly regular basis. It's a heart-wrenching choice. We become rescue workers to save lives. However, we're being forced into the position where we have to choose whose life is more important or more valuable. In a sense you can say that we make that choice every time we go into a building where we're helping people out. But at least with people who are not disabled, we can point them in the direction of the stairs and move on to help others. With a person in a wheelchair, a paraplegic who needs oxygen tanks, we don't have that option."

"What about ladders?" asked Julie. "Why can't you just use the extension ladders to take out those in wheelchairs?"

"Congresswoman," said Jack gently, "we don't have ladders that go that high. That is why we're drawing the line at the fifth floor. Even that's a problem. We need to use those ladders to fight fires, not commit them to helping evacuate people. If they are used in evacuations, more people will die because the fire is spreading."

Seeing the look in the congresswoman's eyes, Jack went on to make another point. "Congresswoman, it is not just terrorist attacks. In 1989 San Francisco experienced a devastating earthquake. In the Transamerica Building the power went off on the forty-eighth floor. People had to walk down more than twenty stories to get to working elevators. Fortunately, there were no casualties. Keep in mind, many of the high-rise buildings in San Francisco are built on landfill. This is not the most stable ground to be on in an earthquake. One person in a wheelchair in the Transamerica Building or any other high-rise can make it extremely difficult to evacuate the building safely."

"Jack," Julie said slowly, "this country has just begun to treat people with disabilities as equals. They have been victims of discrimination for far too long. Some of them still are. Just look at the way you're talking about overweight people. What you're advocating is a dramatic limitation of the rights of the disabled. While I see some sense in what you're saying, I'm not happy about limiting the rights of the disabled for the good of society."

"But Congresswoman," Charles jumped in, "we already limit the rights of the disabled for the good of society. If you are legally blind, you are not allowed to drive. If you have no legs you cannot become a firefighter. This limits the rights of the disabled for the benefit of society as a whole. Yes, what we're advocating would limit the rights of some people to help save the lives of another group of people, rescue personnel. But when we say that the blind cannot become doctors, we are limiting their rights for the good of that segment of society that would be treated by a blind doctor. The disabled are forced to live within their limitations. What we're saying is those limitations should include a restriction on deliberately putting other people at risk."

Julie struggled to control her temper. Through clenched teeth she said, "I'm surprised you're not also advocating that anyone with an infectious disease be forced to have a tattoo on their forehead so that rescue personnel won't give mouth-to-mouth or run other risks of catching the disease."

"That's not fair," replied Jack. "We have reasonable protections against catching an infectious disease. Rescue personnel have rubber gloves, mouth guards, and other equipment that enables them to treat infectious people safely. In a sense, this is the type of safeguard we're asking for. Just as we don't ask paramedics or doctors to recklessly expose themselves to AIDS or other infectious diseases, we shouldn't ask firefighters to risk their lives to save a person in a wheelchair while the building is at risk of crushing hundreds of people. At least not until we have found an alternative way to help rescue people with disabilities."

"What about customers?" asked Julie. "What if a person in a wheelchair is trying to visit a business on the twenty-fifth floor? Would you allow that?"

Jack looked thoughtful. "I hadn't considered that. Realistically, I don't think we would want to go that far in restricting the rights of the disabled . . ."

"And I find it appalling that you are so prejudiced against the overweight," interjected Julie. "You didn't know this, but my best friend when I was growing up was overweight, dangerously so. I watched people pick on him, call him lazy, tell him all he had to do was exercise or eat less. Apart from how much this hurt his feelings, it was all inaccurate. At one point he had his jaw wired shut, but even that didn't work. I've come to the realization that he had a mental illness, just as people with anorexia have an illness. But our society doesn't want to recognize that. We just say that fat people have no self-control. I'm sorry, but it is just not that easy. You are intelligent people. None of you would say that a black person is responsible for his lack of success, but you have no problem saying the same thing about an overweight person. Do you realize how pervasive discrimination against fat people is in our society? Just look at the mass media and the way they portray people. When you're walking down the street and you see someone who is overweight, I'll bet you just avert your eyes and think, why don't you do some exercise? Damn, this really makes me mad."

"I have to admit, Congresswoman," said Jack, "that I hadn't thought about it in this way. You're right, I do have prejudices against fat people and I need to think about that. But you need to think about what we're saying."

Julie just shook her head, trying to control her anger. "Do you realize that airlines charge overweight people for two seats? How is that any different from forcing someone like you, Charles, to sit in the back of the bus? If I were to sponsor an amendment to the ADA it would be to cover the obese, so that they didn't face discrimination."

"Congresswoman," Charles said softly, "I agree with you that something needs to be done about society's attitude toward the overweight. But can you at least acknowledge that we have a point? In today's world, rescue personnel face enough risks. Don't you think we should do everything possible to minimize the risks? That is what we're asking for. Given how strongly we supported you during your previous campaign, don't you think you owe it to us?"

"I'm surprised that you're not asking for mandatory yearly physicals," snorted Julie.

"What do you mean?" asked Jack.

"Well, assume that I'm not classified disabled," said Julie. "According to you, I can safely walk down the stairs while you are helping the injured. How do you know that? What if I've got arthritis? Or a trick knee? Is it going to be best for society if every person shows that they can walk down the stairs and out of the building before they can get a job? And will they have to prove that every year? You seem to be opening a huge can of worms here. And I don't think such restrictions are feasible. Unless, of course, you want to outlaw high-rise buildings."

"Congresswoman, this is a serious subject. You don't seem to believe that, but it is something we feel strongly about." Jack rolled his eyes behind the congresswoman's back.

Julie shook her head. She looked at Meredith. "You've been awfully quiet, Meredith. Why are you here? Are you just window dressing, or do you have some thoughts on this subject?"

Meredith smiled and said, "Actually, I agree with this proposal."

"How could you? After all, women have been victims of discrimination, too. Don't you see, if we take away the rights of the disabled, then we will take away the rights of women and people of color next. I am strongly against that, and I'm strongly against punishing someone or limiting their rights, just because of something over which they have no control, like gender, skin color, or weight or disability," Julie snapped.

"Congresswoman, life is not fair. You will never be able to become president, not because you're a woman, but because you were born in Britain. You had no control over that, but that limits your life. Likewise, your niece had no control over the fact that she was born crippled, but that limits her life. And this will surprise you, but I agree with these guys; we need to get rid of special antidiscrimination programs like affirmative action. They are not helping this country . . ."Before she could complete her thought, Julie interrupted her.

"Meredith, those programs helped you get your job. Do you really think the fire department would have hired women without affirmative action? Because of that program, you are the first female captain in your department. How could you say you want to get rid of these programs?" Julie was aghast.

"Precisely because I am the captain. I work every day with men who don't want to see women on the lines fighting fires. Not because they're sexist, but because women don't have to meet the same physical standards as men. They literally can't pull their own weight. Most of the women in the fire departments in this country don't have to meet the same physical requirements as men and couldn't meet them. That means they can't do the same job. I would like all of these specialized 'women's requirements' abandoned in any job where physical strength is an inherent part of the job. If a woman wants to be a firefighter, she must meet the same requirements as men. That's only fair," Meredith said emphatically.

"What you're advocating would eliminate women firefighters, police officers, carpenters, and any chance of women in combat. You would kill women's sports, like basketball. You paid for college with an athletic scholarship—do you think this country would be better if women's basketball programs were gutted? You would consign women back to the home or to jobs as teachers or nurses. You would put us back fifty years. How can you, a career woman, advocate this?" Julie asked, shocked to her feminist core.

Before Meredith could answer, Jack jumped in. "Actually, Congress-woman, this would not put women back fifty years. There are very few jobs where physical strength is an inherent part. Firefighter yes, and to some extent jobs in the military. But not jobs with the police. My sister is a cop. She is five foot two inches tall, weighs all of a hundred pounds, but is a great cop. Her physical stature actually helps her. For example, we were at a bar, and there was this drunk guy there. I tried to get him to leave us alone, and he got really belligerent with me. He thought he was a great man, and he wanted to fight me. My sister went up to him and told him to stop; he laughed at her. He said that she was too little to stop him. She took him down in ten seconds. He didn't know what hit him. Cops know how to use a suspect's weight against them. My sister uses martial arts techniques. The point is, her stature is an advantage, because the bad guys underestimate her."

"And," said Charles, "as far as women in combat goes, the standards for physical conditioning are nowhere near what they were years ago. Most women can meet the same standards as men. And they should. In the battlefield it would do our side no good if the whole battalion was slowed down because the women couldn't keep up. But those standards would only be for the foot soldiers. In most other jobs, physical strength is not an inherent part of the job. Keep in mind, one military group that still does not have women is the Navy SEALs. This is not because they're sexist; they just refuse to modify their physical standards, and no women have yet passed their tests. The military supports this, as does Congress, because physical strength is such an inherent part of that job. But I would argue that when a woman does pass those tests, she will be seen as a full member of the team. There will be no assumption that she can't do her part. This is a problem today, with firefighters and other positions. Men just assume that women can't do the job, because they have different physical standards to meet than men. And as far as athletics goes, until we fully fund all athletics, I have no problem with cutting some women's programs. After all, we are cutting men's sports to pay for women's programs. That isn't fair, either."

"Charles, I hate to sound like a teacher, but you need to be educated. Title IX does not mandate cutting men's sports to fund women's programs. Title IX is very specific: the school needs to show that it is trying to equalize access to education for women and men. That means all education, not just athletics. Yes, athletics gets the most publicity, but that is not the main thrust of Title IX. Since the passage of Title IX, more women have been offered scholarships of all kinds, including athletic scholarships. More women are going to college. And they are taking all kinds of courses. For example, if my niece decides to be an engineer, she can receive scholarship funding. Twenty-five years ago, she would never have been admitted to an engineering program, let alone received scholarship money. We still have less-qualified men getting scholarship funds for traditionally 'male' programs while highly qualified women students are not receiving any scholarship money."

Charles shook his head. "You can't tell me that men's programs aren't being cut; I've seen it at my son's college. They cut men's wrestling to fund women's volleyball."

"I know that men's programs are being cut, but that isn't the intent of Title IX. That is just school administrators being lazy," said Julie with a sigh. "There are three ways to prove that a school is in compliance with the athletics part of Title IX. You can show that opportunities to participate in athletics are proportionate to their enrollment. For example, if your student body is 40 percent female, then roughly 40 percent of your athletes should be women. Or you can show that your school has a history and continuing practice of offering programs that respond to the interests and abilities of the underrepresented sex. In this part of the test, if we have a former women's college that now admits men, that college has to show that it is expanding programs for men. It doesn't have to happen overnight, but if for the past twenty years there have been men who want a football team, this school had better be trying to build a football team. Likewise, if there is a school that has always admitted both men and women, and the women have consistently wanted a volleyball team, that school can show that they've been trying to build a team but can't find a woman coach, so they're building a team with a man as the coach. It does not meet all of the desires of the women, but the school is trying. The third part of the test is showing that the school meets the desires of women student athletes even when there are proportionately fewer women than men participating in sports. For example, if you have roughly 50 percent men and women at your college, but only 10 percent of the women are interested in sports, you do need to meet the demands of those women. That doesn't mean that you have to offer every women's sport imaginable, but you do need to meet the demands for women's athletics. The important thing is that you only have to meet one of the criteria to comply with Title IX. Now some schools just cut men's programs to fund women's programs. That is the easy way out, and it creates a great deal of resentment. But the bottom line is that it is wrong to fund a program for ten male wrestlers when there are fifty women who want a basketball team and the college says there isn't enough money."

"Well, Congresswoman," said Charles, "while I appreciate the lesson, the fact of the matter is that schools across the country are losing money. They are cutting men's teams and funding women's teams. The men's teams bring in money through attendance at events and alumni donations. That hurts education for everyone."

"Charles," smiled Julie, "I'll send you some fact sheets. One thing to realize is that sports like men's wrestling don't bring in much money through either attendance or alumni donations. It takes time to bring in the money. There are women's teams that do bring in more money than men's teams. For example, the women's basketball program at the University of Colorado is more successful than the men's basketball program. Also, only approximately 10 percent of men's football teams make money for their college. However, these teams absorb huge amounts of money. They have, on average, twice the number of players as a pro ball team. That is ludicrous. Just cutting some of those players would fund women's teams in many sports. As more women graduate and go on to careers, they will give donations for scholarships that support women's sports. As a direct result of Title IX, we now have the Women's NBA. We have women winning gold medals at the Olympics in such 'male' sports as ice hockey and soccer. These women are role models for young girls today. Rather than getting rid of Title IX, I think it should be expanded."

"Okay, Congresswoman." Charles held up his hands in defeat. "I'll give you Title IX, and I look forward to reading your fact sheets. But I won't give up on amending the ADA. I don't think you can ask rescue personnel to put their lives on the line for disabled people who want the right to live or work wherever they want. It is not socially responsible."

Julie rolled her eyes. "The bottom line is the changes you're advocating would mean women would lose the chance to become firefighters or fight in the military. I can't support anything that would limit the ability of women to compete for the jobs they want."

Meredith looked at the congresswoman. "Actually, not all women would lose the chance to do these jobs. Only women who could not meet the physical standards. For example, I can meet the same standards as the men. I'm a big woman and I work out, keep in shape. It's true, most women would not be able to pass the physical test. But what you're forgetting is most men can't meet that test either. Look at it this way: Did you have to meet the same requirements as your opponent to win this election? Did the media take it easy on you because you're a woman? Did the district award you extra votes because you're a woman and there aren't many women in Congress?"

"Don't be ridiculous," snapped Julie. "I won the election based on merit. No one gave me anything."

"That is exactly what we're advocating, Congresswoman," replied Meredith. "When women are given extra help, they are not respected in their jobs. The same goes for people of color. I would argue this way: The vast majority of people, men and women, who run for office, don't win. They lose because the better-qualified person gets the job. But if we start appointing people to office to address historic imbalances, this country will go downhill fast. However, we have no problem doing that in business or education. That is fundamentally wrong."

Julie shook her head. "So you want me to abolish affirmative action and gut the Americans with Disabilities Act. We need to do this to ensure fairness and safety in our society. Using your logic, we should ban integration. If we allow people of color to attend traditionally all-white schools or move into all-white neighborhoods, there will be social unrest and police might get killed. I'm sorry, but when you take some jobs you know there is a risk involved. Likewise, government must step in to help groups that have been subject to systematic discrimination. Society will not change unless government forces it to. And just because you supported me in the last election does not mean I am bound to do what you want. Your support got you into this office to present your proposal. I owe it to myself and the country to do what is in the best interest of the country, not what is in your best interest."

Points to Ponder

Agree or disagree with the following statements, and give your reasons:

1. Jack and Charles are right—it is wrong to further risk the lives of rescue personnel by allowing the obese or disabled to live or work on the highest floors of high-rise buildings.

2. Julie wants to get reelected and needs the support of the firefighters. She should agree to their proposal.

3. The disabled have been denied rights for far too long. It would be wrong to ask them to limit their lives further.

4. The disabled can live full lives without working at the top of tall buildings.

5. If we limit the disabled in this way, soon firemen and rescue personnel will want them allowed only on the ground floors of buildings. Next they will want the disabled to live only in designated disabled complexes. New limits will keep coming until the disabled have no rights.

6. If we limit the rights of the disabled in this way, we will start to limit the rights of other groups. For example, people with asthma would also have trouble walking down seventy stories.

7. When rights clash, as in this scenario, the rights of the majority should prevail. There are more rescue personnel than disabled, and they

provide service to society as a whole, so their rights should supersede those of the disabled.

8. This type of restriction would inevitably lead to persons with disabilities being prevented from using businesses on the higher floors of buildings.

9. No one's rights are absolute in this country. Therefore the rights of the disabled should be limited for the good of society as a whole.

10. Affirmative action should be eliminated. All it does is create more discrimination in society.

11. Without affirmative action, we would go back to white males controlling everything in this country.

12. If the ADA is modified in this way, there will be no incentive to change. The best way to solve this problem would be more federal funding to find better ways to evacuate a building.

13. The overweight are responsible for their disability; Julie's comparison of the overweight with black people is not valid.

14. While some men's programs have been cut as a result of Title IX, overall it has been more positive than negative.

15. Women in this country get all the benefits of citizenship without having to pay the price for those benefits because they don't get drafted like men could. If women want to be considered full citizens, they should be willing to be drafted and defend our country, just like the men.

Essay Questions

1. Discuss the ways government should respond when the civil rights of one group conflict with the civil rights of another. How should these choices be made? Should the majority or the minority be protected?

2. Discuss the ways the government could or should deal with problems of prejudice or discrimination. How can the government ensure equality for all?

Chapter 5

Having Our Say:
Public Opinion

Good morning, everyone. What's on the agenda today?" asked Governor Jeremiah Turner, looking at his aide, Meagan Creasy.

Meagan smiled and shook her head. "Governor, I don't know how you can be so cheery at seven a.m. Paul Maurice is here with the results of last night's poll. He wants to talk to you before you do anything else. Then there are several bills waiting for your signature, and members of your party want to see you. I've tentatively set them for eight o'clock. They're not happy about that, but you did say you wanted to see Paul Maurice first thing this morning."

"Good. Show PM in, and tell the party hacks I'll see them for breakfast at eight." The governor walked to his desk, dropped his briefcase, and then looked over the bills still awaiting his signature. The door opened, and Paul Maurice Picket walked in.

"Good morning, Governor. How are you?" asked the pollster.

"I'll be better once I've seen the poll numbers. What does it look like?" asked the governor.

"Not as good as it could. Your job approval ratings are down again. So are the approval ratings for your party. The public is finding it difficult to accept what they see as your indecisiveness." Paul Maurice glanced at the governor to see how he was taking the bad news. The governor seemed unfazed.

"They'll come up; the public just has to get used to doing things a new way. I want to see the numbers on police funding. The legislature is screaming for me to act on the bill. I've got to make a decision today whether to sign it or not. What does the public say?" Governor Turner sipped from his coffee as he looked at Picket.

"Not surprisingly, the polls are split. When asked if they would like to see more police on the streets, 80 percent of those polled approved. However, when asked if they would be willing to pay another five cents a gallon for gas to pay for the new cops, 80 percent said no. So the public wants you to put more police on the street, but they don't want to pay for it." Paul Maurice looked at the governor.

Jeremiah Turner shook his head. "Those poll results haven't changed in a week. Is it possible that the questions you're asking are the problem?"

"No, sir, the questions are straightforward, not biased in any way. The first question is 'Do you think there should be more police on the streets?' and the second question is 'Would you be willing to pay another five cents a gallon for gas to pay for more police on the streets?' These questions are straightforward; there is no risk of bias," Paul Maurice replied smugly. He knew his job.

"Well, what if you asked something like 'Would you be willing to pay slightly more for gasoline in order to decrease crime?' Why don't you change the wording of the question to reflect the intent of the bill?" Governor Turner was frustrated.

"Well, Governor, then there would be bias in the question. For some people, five cents a gallon is a slight increase. For others it is not. And that question assumes more police will decrease crime; that might not be the case. It will mean more criminals are likely to be caught, but that would not necessarily decrease crime. To decrease crime you need to get to the causes of crime, like poverty or greed. More cops won't do that, and the question would then be misleading. Some people would think that the increased tax would go to pay for after-school programs or antipoverty programs. So I don't think we should change the question. You'll just have to make your decision based on this information." Paul Maurice shook his head. This job paid well, but it really was a headache.

"What about the National Guard call-up?" asked the governor.

"What about it?" replied Paul Maurice, confused by the question.

"Do you think we should run a poll on this? Ask the public whether or not I should call up the units in this state, in response to the president's request?" Jeremiah asked seriously.

"Um . . . Governor . . . I don't know about that one. I'm not an attorney, but I don't think you've got any choice on that. The president requested the troops. He is commander in chief of the armed forces of this country. Realistically, what would you do if the polls showed the state didn't support the National Guard call-up? Would you refuse to call up the troops?" Paul Maurice winced inwardly.

The governor sighed. "I hadn't thought of that. Thanks, PM. I'll give it some thought. You'll give me the poll results on gay rights tomorrow?"

Paul Maurice nodded his head as he left the office. Meagan smiled at him and then led the delegation of party leaders into the governor's office.

"Good morning, Marlon, Jacob, Joyce. What brings you here on this fine morning?" The governor looked at the party delegation without concern. "Why the big rush for the meeting? By the way, what do you think of my running a poll to see what the people of the state feel about the National Guard call-up? Paul Maurice thinks it would be a bad idea."

"Polls, Governor, polls are the reason for this meeting," Marlon said somberly. "We in the party want to talk to you about polls. A poll on the National Guard call-up would be political suicide. If the public says no to a call-up and you follow the public's desire, you will be impeached. You're relying too much on polls. You need to make some decisions yourself. And you need to call up the National Guard."

"Marlon," replied the governor with a sigh, "we've had this discussion before. I don't want to have it again."

"Well, governor," interjected Joyce Lincoln, "I haven't had this discussion with you before, and so we will have it now. The poll results are terrible. The public perception of the party and of you personally is continually falling. Not only does the public feel that you are indecisive and unable to do the job, they are tarring all members of the party with the same brush. This has got to stop. And I agree with Marlon—you must call up the National Guard. If you don't, you may not be impeached, but this state will be the laughingstock of the country."

"Joyce, it is just going to take the public some time," responded the governor. "I realize that the poll results are not good for the party right now, but the people of this state need to realize that I was serious when I was campaigning. I will respond to their wishes and make no major policy decisions without getting their opinion first. Once they realize that this is actually a more democratic way of running the state, that their opinion does matter, the poll numbers will come back up. And I think we should get some feedback about the National Guard call-up. After all, the people called up have relatives in this state. They have legitimate concerns about the call-up. Also, in my humble opinion, I don't *have* to call up the National Guard. As far as I'm concerned, federalism is strong and viable in the United States. And as part of federalism, the states are part of the checks and balances. Although the Constitution makes the president commander in chief, he must convince the governors of the need for the National Guard. If we don't agree, then that is federalism."

"Jeremiah, I'm sorry," said Joyce as she shook her head, "but you're not being realistic. The people of this state didn't send you here to be their lackey; they sent you here to do a job. Waiting to see how the public feels on any given issue is not the way to do the job. They do expect you to use your brain. That is why you are seen as a representative of the people. You are here to do their work for them."

"Yes, Joyce, I know. But as their representative, I can't do their work for them if I don't know what they want. I disagree with you. The fundamental job of a representative is to do what the people want, not to do what I want. The people voted for me because they wanted to be able to influence decisions. They believed me when I told them that I would ask for and respond to their opinion. I need to respect that." The governor could see that he wasn't convincing Joyce or the other party members.

"Jeremiah, you're a novice to politics," Jacob weighed in. "You were elected because you weren't associated with the scandal of campaign funding that tainted everyone in the last Assembly. You are a successful businessman, but you've never been involved in politics. You don't realize that the public just wants government to work; they don't want to have to pay attention to it. Polls are a tool. But they are only a tool. They show you what the people think about an issue at that moment. However, people's attitudes change rapidly. If you ask Picket, you will find that the same question asked over a period of a year will elicit different results, because the public looks at something a new way, they have new facts, or the issue is no longer leading the news. Now, because of the kidnapping and murder of little Jesse Griffin, there is an outcry for more police. However, more police wouldn't have saved Jesse. It is almost impossible to prevent a stranger kidnapping, particularly when the offender has never done such a thing before. If you put more police on the street, people are just going to say you're inefficient. There will be another Jesse, and all those new police won't stop it. But the people will complain about all their tax money being spent on police who can't stop crime. They will also complain about the fact that funds are being reallocated to the police from other social programs. The public has a short attention span; you can't rely on polls to make all of your decisions."

"I disagree with you, Jacob," replied the governor stubbornly. "It is true that I'm new to government, but the reason the people elected me is I gave them a chance to get involved in government. I do think that they will do the right thing, the best thing for this state. If I give them the chance, they will help us turn this state into one of the best-run states in the union. As a matter of fact, the demonstrations in support of my environment bill are an expression of the people. They are getting involved in government. When 100,000 people feel strongly enough about an issue to come out and demonstrate, I think we have to listen."

"So you think that the public supports environmentalism just because 100,000 people were at the plaza holding signs?" asked Marlon. "Do you know that at least 40 percent of them were hired to be here?"

"What are you talking about?" asked the governor.

"There are companies that will provide demonstrators for your cause. Many of these people don't necessarily support the cause, but they are hired for the day, come out and demonstrate, and then go home." Marlon smirked at the governor.

"But that's ridiculous. How are we supposed to know what the people want if some of the demonstrators are hired?" asked the governor, confused. "Anyway, the people of this state are fundamentally good. They will support my gay rights bill."

"Really, Governor?" asked Jacob with a smile. "You really think the people of this state will do the right thing? When you campaigned you advocated full equality for gays in this state, including marriage and all rights that accompany that institution. Have you seen what the people of the state think of your bill?"

"No. As a matter of fact, Paul Maurice has been having a difficult time getting poll numbers on that for me. It seems that he can only do so many polls a day, and it always seems there are other things that need to be asked. He did promise me numbers on that tomorrow. But I don't see any problem. The people knew I supported gay rights, and they elected me." Jeremiah looked at Jacob, wondering why he looked so smug.

"I'm sorry to tell you that Paul Maurice has not been quite as forthcoming as you would like," said Jacob. "He has actually done three polls on the issue. The first one, three weeks ago, asked if the respondents supported your gay rights initiative. Seventy percent said no. The second one, two weeks ago, asked if they supported equality for gays. Fifty-five percent said no. Last week the question was, 'Should the governor continue to push for a gay rights initiative?' A full 80 percent said no. The follow-up questions all show the same thing. While the people support equality on a theoretical level, they do not support equal rights for gays, especially not gay marriage. They want you to focus on other things, like education, the environment, and employment. Paul Maurice has been running polls constantly trying to get the results you want."

"That can't be true!" exclaimed the governor. "The public knew when they elected me that I was strongly committed to gay rights. There must be something wrong with the polls."

"No, Governor," replied Joyce, "there is nothing wrong with the polls. The public does not support gay rights in this state. They voted for you in spite of your standing on gay rights, not because of it. They like things in the abstract, not in reality. Members of the legislature are getting all kinds of letters opposed to this initiative. They are outnumbering the favorable letters eleven to one. I would imagine that Meagan could probably tell you the same about the letters you're receiving."

"Marlon, is this true?" asked the governor.

"Yes, Jeremiah, it is true. The bottom line is, you cannot run government like a business. In a business you have to give the people what they want or they go somewhere else. Sometimes in government you have to tell the people what they want, or even do what is best for them when they don't want it. If all members of our government relied solely on polls to make their decisions, black people and women would not be able to vote, the Civil Rights Act would never have been passed, segregation would still be with us, and only white Christians would be citizens. People in office need to use their brains and do what is in the best interests of their constituents, not what the people want." Marlon shook his head at the naiveté of the governor.

Joyce jumped into the discussion again. "Governor, you must realize that polls simplify things too much. For example, the economy of this state is not doing well. There are numerous options available. A tax cut is the most obvious, but that will also mean cutting public services. Or, we could try to lure businesses here from other states by giving corporate tax breaks. But that commits us to giving businesses tax breaks for a minimum of twenty years. That can hurt us later, when the economy slows again. In addition, we run the risk of other states trying to lure our businesses. Also, we would get population movements to the locations of the new business, reducing established tax bases. If we give tax breaks to new businesses, established businesses will also want breaks in order to be competitive. If we can't help out established businesses, we can appeal to the federal government for help with a grant-in-aid, but it usually comes with strings attached. We could float a bond issue, but bonds must be paid off eventually. Now, how would you present these options to the people of this state in a poll? Most of the people wouldn't understand the ramifications of these policy initiatives, and they wouldn't be able to make an informed decision."

"But what about democracy?" asked the governor. "As elected officials, don't we need to respond to the public?"

"Governor," replied Marlon, "the public is an ass. In the abstract they want to be involved in decision making. However, when it comes down to reality, most people do not want to have to pay attention to government. They do not want to respond to the polls. Are you aware of the fact that at least 50 percent of the people in this state are refusing to participate in the polls PM is constantly running? They can't be bothered."

The governor looked aghast. "That can't be right. The polls run during the campaign were consistent. More than 80 percent of the public were in favor of having a direct impact on state government by giving their opinion. How could so many people now refuse to participate?"

"They're tired and busy, Governor," replied Joyce. "I am, too. My house has been called three times in the past two months on these polls. The calls come at dinnertime when we're trying to be together as a family. They last at least twenty minutes. I'm actively involved in politics, but even *I* am getting fed up. My husband got the last call and refused to participate. He wants no part of this, and many other citizens in the state are feeling the same way."

The governor shook his head. "What is wrong with people? Your husband should want to participate, have his voice heard. I'll talk to PM about changing the time the pollsters call."

Joyce snorted in exasperation. "That won't solve the problem, Governor. Most people work during the day, so the calls must be in the evening. You can't call too late, because some people will be in bed. You just can't rely on polls to make all of your decisions. People are saying anything to get the pollsters off their backs."

"What do you mean?" asked the governor.

Marlon sighed. "I was with an old friend when he was polled on your diversity program. This guy is really a racist. I was listening to him answer the questions, and he gave answers that surprised me. I asked him about it, and he said he didn't want the questioner to know that he felt blacks and Mexicans were inferior. He was afraid word would get out and his business would be hurt. People sometimes tell the pollster the politically correct answer rather than what they really think."

"But that taints the process!" exclaimed the governor.

"Yes, Governor. That is why you need to make the decision, not rely on the polls," replied Joyce.

"Maybe what we need is more information . . . ," mused the governor. "I'll talk to PM about doing a media campaign, educating the public about the importance of these polls. We can also educate the public about major policy areas so they can make informed decisions when giving their answers to the pollsters. I'm sure the people of this state would support gay rights if they knew the problems of discrimination that gays face."

Joyce shook her head. The governor continued, "Did you know that gays are being denied medical treatment because of their sexuality? Really. Some doctors are refusing to treat gays because they disagree with homosexuality. That is flat-out wrong. I had a letter here from a woman. Her partner was hospitalized for AIDS. The hospital refuses to let this woman see her partner because the family has decided that they want to make all decisions. This woman has no legal recourse. She has been mother to the couple's children for ten years. However, because her partner is the biological mother, this woman has no parental rights. The kids might be put in foster care. Surely if the public knew about things like this, they would support my gay rights program."

"Governor," said Joyce, "I support your stand on gay rights. You are right that they are being discriminated against and changes must be made. However, the public is uncomfortable with this, so your polls will never give you the support you want. This is what we've been trying to tell you: you need to lead the public, not be led by them."

"Joyce, I'm sorry, I just disagree with you," replied the governor. "I have faith in the people of this state. They will do the right thing if they are educated about the problem. For example, I know that the majority of the people in this state support the Aardvarks. They were thrilled when the Aardvarks won the championship. But very few people in this state support the riots that took place after the game." The governor paused to see the reactions of the party members.

"Your point, Governor?" asked Marlon. "Are you going to take a poll to see if you should ban riots after a championship game?"

"No, Marlon, I'm not," snapped the governor. "I'm going to propose a new law. The team will be responsible for the damages caused by rioters; costs of the riot will come out of the salary cap. This way the fans won't riot; they won't want to cost their team money. I'm sure the good people of this state will support such a law."

The party leaders looked at the governor incredulously. "You *are* kidding, aren't you?" asked Jacob. "You can't seriously think you can hold a team liable for the actions of the fans."

"I can and I do, Jacob," grinned the governor. "The principle is not unique. After all, we hold gun manufacturers responsible for the harm caused by their guns. This is the same thing. You do realize that the rioters caused $2 million in damages and cost the state more than $500,000 in additional police costs, don't you? There is no reason that the state budget must be subjected to this when a few fans got too unruly. If the team were liable, they would educate the fans and do whatever was necessary to prevent these outbreaks of violence. We need to go back to the time when a win was celebrated with a parade, not a riot."

"Governor," sighed Joyce, "I agree with you that these riots are terrible. They have done untold damage to this state. However, I don't think this is the best way to solve the problem. Essentially, you will be telling the Aardvarks to lose every game to prevent the possibility of riots when they win. If not that, then the Aardvarks will just move to another state that does not have this liability law."

"I doubt it, Joyce," smiled the governor. "I think this will be a model for other states. They will all implement laws like this. Then the violence will stop. I think the people of this state will support me in this."

Marlon looked at the governor with disgust. "Governor, you cannot legislate people's emotions. They will riot whether or not the Aardvarks will be financially responsible for the damages. People don't change."

"Yes, Marlon," replied the governor, "people do change. Don't you re-member the Stanley Cup playoffs in '92?"

"I have no idea what you're talking about, Governor," replied Marlon. The others in the office also looked confused.

"The Florida Panthers had a player, I don't remember his name, but he was having a bad streak." The governor paused, and the party members looked at him. "One night, before the game, he saw a rat in the locker room. He took a swipe at the rat with his stick. He went on to have a great game. The fans heard about it, and after that, whenever the Pan-thers scored, hundreds of plastic rats were thrown on the ice. It was a great show of fan support, but it took a long time to clean up all the rats. The playoff games were really delayed because of it."

"Your point escapes me, Governor," said Marlon. "This just seems to support my point, that you can't change people."

"Actually, Marlon, this story shows you can change people," replied the governor smugly. "During the off-season there was a change in the rules. If the fans littered the ice, their team would receive a penalty for delay of game. Now there are no rats thrown on the ice in Florida. Fans are so supportive of their team that they won't do things to harm the team. We see it in soccer, too: penalties are given to teams when their fans act up, and this eliminates that problem."

"Governor," grimaced Jacob, "the people of this state ardently support their team. They are not going to support a law that will harm the Aard-varks financially. You would have to push this law through against their will. That assumes, of course, that this is a good law."

"It *is* a good law," snapped the governor. "And you're wrong: the people of this state will support it. Once they realize that this law will stop the ri-oting and postgame violence, they will do what is right. Also, given what you've said here, I think I'll ask Paul Maurice to start tracking emails and letters. This way I can get a better feel for the views of the public."

"Governor," said Marlon through clenched teeth, "that is not going to solve the problem. Only a certain type of person will write letters, so you will not be getting a representative sampling of public opinion. And as far as emails go, the problem there is you don't know where the people live. You could be responding to emails from people in another state. You might just as well respond solely to interest groups that claim to be representing the opinion and views of the public. Or you could even push for an amendment to the state constitution so that we could adopt the initiative process to allow the public to influence government, as some other states do. Those initiatives allow the public to participate, but they also create huge problems. Too many of them are irresponsible or even unconstitutional. The public is too ignorant to be directly involved in governing."

Jeremiah shook his head. "I find it hard to believe that you have all been active in politics for so long with these attitudes. How do you expect politicians to get reelected if they don't respond to the will of the public? After all, this is a democracy."

The party leaders groaned. The governor just didn't get it.

Points to Ponder

Agree or disagree with the following statements, and give your reasons:

1. Public opinion polls are not accurate barometers of what the public wants. Politicians should ignore them.

2. Public opinion polls are the easiest way for politicians to find out what the public is concerned about. Politicians should give them greater weight.

3. John Stuart Mill said that the trouble with democracy is that the people get the government they deserve. Public opinion polls should be binding on elected officials as a way of showing the public how it is sometimes wrong.

4. Politicians should always use their best judgment, even if that often means breaking campaign promises and going against what the public wants.

5. Governor Turner should push through his gay rights initiative. The public knew he supported it when they elected him, and the fact that their opinion has now changed should be irrelevant.

6. Pollsters can change public opinion just by changing the question asked. Therefore we should generally ignore public opinion polls.

7. Politicians who pander to public opinion are not doing their job; they're just trying to get reelected.

8. Polls do not always reflect public opinion, because many Americans don't know enough about an issue or are unwilling to give an answer that might make them look bad.

9. Polls simplify complex issues. While they can reflect the public view of a simple question, they cannot give reliable information on complex issues.

10. Although most issues the government deals with are complex, the American public is intelligent enough to understand the issues. Politicians simply do not want to make the effort to really listen to the public.

11. The governor is right. We need a law that holds teams responsible for the damage caused by rioting fans.

12. Polls are just a harmless way for politicians to give the public the impression that it has a say in government. Most politicians don't care about public opinion.

13. Letters and emails come from concerned citizens, citizens who take time out of their busy schedules to tell politicians their feelings. Politicians need to pay more attention to them.

14. Interest groups are one way concerned citizens can tell politicians their feelings on a matter. It would be appropriate for Jeremiah to pay attention to them to find out what the public thinks.

15. Marlon is wrong. Initiatives are a legitimate way for the public to influence the government and are particularly valuable in a democracy.

Essay Questions

1. The founding principle of democracy is rule by the people. It is impossible for public representatives to implement the people's desires if the representatives don't know what those desires are. Therefore, should

public opinion polls, demonstrations, letters, and emails be considered valid expressions of the people's will and be binding on elected representatives?

2. Discuss the problems associated with public opinion and its influence on the government.

Chapter 6

Culture in a Country of Immigrants: Political Socialization

Pat Richardson shook her head. She really hated going to her in-laws' house for the monthly family gathering. They were so old-country. Even though they were born in the U.S., it was like they lived in Europe in the 1920s. Didn't these people realize that the world had changed? She looked at her reflection one last time, patted her hair into place, and gathered the children. They all joined her husband Rick in the car. The twenty-minute ride to his parents' home was silent; the kids hated going there also.

Taking a deep breath, Pat followed Rick and the kids into the house. "Hi Mom, Dad. How have you been?"

"All right, I suppose," Frank snorted. But I tell you, this country is going to hell in a handbasket. The government just isn't doing its job anymore. I've lived here all my life, paid my taxes, and now, in my so-called golden years, the government is just making my life more difficult. They've cut our Medicare benefits again and Social Security is not going up as much as it should. Instead, they're giving more money to those deadbeats who won't get a job."

"Gramps, you know the government cannot support every program," said Tommy. "There's only so much tax money to go around. The government does have to help out the poor."

"Not at our expense! We should be taken care of first," interrupted Lila. "You kids don't realize how many sacrifices we've made for this country. It is the government's responsibility to take care of us."

Pat shook her head. The in-laws were in rare form tonight. It was going to be a long night. Tommy continued to try to reason with his grandparents.

"Gran, what would you rather have: more money for you, or more money for kids to go to college? If more kids go to college, they can get better jobs, pay higher taxes, and then the government can give more to help older folks like you and Gramps."

"By the time all you guys get jobs that pay enough to support higher taxes, we'll be dead. And if we're not, the government will just spend the money elsewhere," replied Lila.

"Besides, the government shouldn't be making that choice with our money. We paid into Social Security, we should get that money back—the government shouldn't be using it to pay for other programs," Frank jumped in.

"Not quite, Gramps. First of all, Social Security was always intended as a supplement, not the primary support for retirees. Also, I'll bet you've taken out much more than you put in. When you were working the rates were much lower. I'll bet between the two of you, you contributed less than five thousand dollars into Social Security. Does that sound about right?" asked Tommy.

Frank nodded grudgingly. Tommy continued, "How much have you two received in government payments so far? You've been retired for 20 years. I don't know how much your monthly checks are, but I'll ballpark it low—figure an average of $500 each a month. Let's see . . . 20 years times 12 months a year equals 240 months. At $500 a month that's $120,000 each. Now if you had invested that $5,000 you contributed, you might not have earned as high a return. Like so many other people, you and Gran have taken out much more than you've put into Social Security. That is why the government isn't giving you large increases in your payments. It can't afford to. You're taking money from other necessary programs." Tommy glanced at his grandfather, afraid he was going to have a heart attack.

"Like those programs for foreigners. Those damned Mexicans down the street! They're killing the property values. Look at all those cars on their lawn. They're having another party. The music, if you can call it music, is blasting all the time. And the smells! I swear they eat garbage. And they breed like rabbits. They already have four kids, and she's got another bun in the oven. They're all probably getting welfare, sucking off the public tit, taking money that should go to help us out." Frank, at 80 years old, was not the most tolerant of people. He also refused to acknowledge any of Tommy's points. Pat shook her head and turned to Lila, her mother-in-law, waiting for the next round of poison.

Lila chimed in, as if on cue, "I don't know why our government lets them come here. They'll never become good Americans. They just leech off our social programs and never work. They don't do anything for this country."

Tommy attempted to reason with his grandparents again. "Gran, that's the same thing they said about our people, when the Irish first came here. There was a lot of hatred for the Irish, but now we're held up as model immigrants."

"It's not the same thing. The Irish brought good values to this country. Those wetbacks don't." Lila looked disapprovingly at her grandson.

"Yes, they do," replied Tommy stubbornly. "You're always going on about how no one respects values anymore. The Mexicans do. They have strong family values. They respect their elders and don't want to do things that would bring shame to their families. Very few teenage Mexican American girls get pregnant, and if they do, the guy is forced by the community to marry the girl. You don't have a lot of unwed mothers like you do in white society, at least not in the first generation. After they've been here for several generations they become like people who've been in America longer, with all of our cultural values and problems, like unwed mothers and promiscuous young men trying to father as many children as possible."

"Yeah? Well, what about their gangs? Are you trying to tell me they're good for this country?" Frank was disgusted with the thought that Mexican Americans could actually share some of his values.

"What about the Irish gangs 150 years ago?" countered Tommy. "The Mexicans are doing exactly what the Irish did—forming gangs to protect themselves from the hatred of mainstream society. The gangs and other associations like their friendship clubs help immigrants learn about American culture and norms. And another thing, the Mexicans are very religious. You're always saying that not enough people go to church in this country. The Mexicans do."

"Well, they don't become Americans. They don't learn the language, the customs, they don't share our beliefs," Frank grumbled.

"It takes time, Dad," ventured Pat. "My grandparents came over from Lithuania and didn't know anything about this country. They didn't speak English or know the customs. When they died, they were still more comfortable with speaking Lithuanian. But my mom is bilingual. She learned a lot about American customs at school, in church, from her friends. And I grew up here. This country is all I know. Are you saying that I'm not a true American?"

Frank shook his head, "No, of course not. But you wanted to learn. They don't. They keep their old customs and don't accept ours."

"Really, Gramps?" asked Nora sweetly. She knew she was her grandfather's favorite and could get away with a lot. "You mean they should celebrate that great 'American' holiday, St. Patrick's Day? You know how you like to see the Chicago River dyed green on St. Paddy's day. They have the 'American' right to celebrate their culture just like the Irish, the Poles, and the Asians. Like Mom said, in time their kids will be just as American as the rest of us. . . . By the way," Nora grinned wickedly, "would you like to be paying triple or quadruple prices for your food?"

"What in the hell are you talking about, child?" Frank looked at her with alarm. Inflation had hit them so badly that all the retirement planning seemed to have been wasted.

"Well, Gramps," Nora continued, "those 'damn Mexicans' are the ones working in the fields ten or twelve hours a day, picking crops. They're also the ones working in the canneries and food processing plants. They do that work for minimum wage. That keeps your food prices low. Last year Mom decided to make her own pickles, and she had all of us out in the fields picking cucumbers. I tell you, I never want to do that again. I was only out there three hours. My back was killing me, I was sunburned, and bugs flew up my nose. There is no way I would do that kind of work for minimum wage. But the Mexicans do that and all kinds of other jobs white people don't want, like janitor, maid, and the grunt work for society. Just like the Irish did when they came to this country. We wouldn't have this standard of living if we didn't have the Mexicans."

"Child," Frank shook his head sadly, "I don't know what they're teaching you in school these days . . ."

"The same as they taught you, Gramps," Nora said with a little touch of sarcasm. "How to be an American. By the way, Mom, I wanted to ask you a lawyer question." Pat rolled her eyes. She didn't know what was coming, but she knew her daughter. Nora was on a roll and wanted to make trouble. You would think that a college freshman would have learned when to just let it go. The grandparents were going to make this evening miserable enough without Nora stirring the pot. "What do you think of the Assak case? Will that defense work? Is it constitutional? We were discussing it in my government class, and there were a lot of different opinions."

Pat sighed as her father-in-law snorted, "Throw the damned towelheads out of this country. Send them back to the desert where they belong!"

Pat glared at her daughter but said sweetly, "Nora, that is really complex. I don't think it is suitable conversation for a dinner with your grandparents."

Before Nora could reply, Lila jumped in, "Actually, Pat, I would like to know what you think. You're not just a lawyer, but, as you are so proud of saying, you're a liberal feminist. What *do* you think of the case?"

Pat gathered her thoughts. "It's complex. Our legal system mandates that it is a crime for a thirteen-year-old girl to be married to a twenty-eight-year-old man. The legal age of marriage in this state is seventeen. The girl's parents are charged with child abuse and the 'husband' is charged with statutory rape. But it is also true that in many Arab and Muslim cultures girls are married at puberty. Therefore Assak and the girl's parents are saying that no crime was committed. They're saying that this is a freedom-of-religion issue, as it is part of their religion that a girl marry early to ensure her virginity on the wedding night. I *am* a feminist, so it really bothers me to think that a girl should only be valued if she is a virgin on her wedding night. I also don't think a thirteen-year-old is old enough or mature enough to consent to a marriage, which is the claim in this case. But I do think we have to respect the cultures that exist in this country. If we prosecute all cultural differences, we will hurt its diversity and multiculturalism. For example, I can see some loony psychologist arguing that it is bad for the sexual development of girls to remain virgins until they are at least eighteen. I don't think it is wrong for parents to pass on their cultural values to their children—I think that is the primary job of the parent. And if Assak and this girl's family were still living in the Middle East, no one would have a problem with the marriage."

Sean jumped into the discussion. "But Mom, in the church youth group, Father Juan said that the Assaks were wrong, that Islam does not mandate that a girl be married so young. He said that Islam mandates modesty for both men and women, not this stuff that the woman must be a virgin or her family can kill her."

"That's true, Sean. But religion changes with the culture of the region. And that is what Assak's lawyers are arguing, that this is his regional religious culture. But I worry about using culture as a defense. If Assak gets off, then we will have two standards of law in this country. Muslims will not be prosecuted for child abuse because of the cultural defense, but non-Muslims will be prosecuted. I don't like the thought of something like this developing. There was a case last year, for example. A ten-year-old girl was mutilated. Her grandmother cut off her clitoris, in accordance with their religious and cultural beliefs. What we call female genital mutilation they call an essential religious belief. In that case the jury found the grandmother not guilty. Assak's attorney is drawing on that case for his defense. This worries me, as a mother and a lawyer. In another case, a girl was protesting against an arranged marriage. The parents wanted the marriage to keep wealth in the family, but the girl wanted no part of it. Realistically, arranged marriages are traditional; it is only recently that love marriages were considered normal. But I don't know if we should use culture as a legal defense. If we establish precedents like this, who knows where this country will end up?" Pat closed her eyes and waited. She knew that her in-laws would respond. Before they could, Tommy jumped in.

"Isn't the problem that they don't have enough gangs and immigrant associations in this country, Mom? I mean, if they were like the Mexicans or Asians, the Muslims already here would have associations that could have told the Assaks that their behavior is not allowed in this country." Tommy looked at his mother, but before she could formulate a reply, her father-in-law interrupted.

"That's what we get for letting all these foreigners in here," Frank growled. "If we just let in white people from Europe, and none of those coloreds, this country would be much better off."

"Well, Dad," Rick responded, "That kind of ignores the benefits this country gained from slavery. It also wouldn't take care of the Indian problem."

"Rick, I can't believe you said that! We've discussed this too many times!" cried Pat.

"I'm sorry, Pat," her husband continued, "but you don't see them like I do. I have to work with those Indians all the time. That is, when they work. They work on 'Indian time.' They show up when they want to. Yesterday John Redbear didn't show up. You know why? He was helping a lady fix her car. He didn't even know this woman. She had broken down on the freeway, so he spent most of the day helping her fix her car. Because of that, I was short one man on the job. We all had to work through lunch to get the job done."

"But, Dad," gasped Nora, "what if that had been me? Wouldn't you have wanted someone to stop and help me if I was broken down? You know in those valleys cell phones don't work half the time. Wasn't John doing what you say we should all do? Practice Christian charity and help someone in need? You're always complaining about how no one is willing to help others, no one is willing to get involved. Indians generally put helping people above work—isn't that a value that should be stronger in this society? And what about the environment? They're so focused on cleaning up the environment. Isn't that good for this country?"

Rick shook his head. "I agree with your grandfather. They're teaching you strange things in that school. By helping one person, John hurt twenty men on my crew. Where is the good in that? And don't give me that environmental crap. You wouldn't believe how much the EPA complicates my job."

"But, Dad," said Tommy, "if we don't clean up the environment, you'll never get to go fishing in the North River again. You've always told me how much you and Gramps enjoyed that. I want to go fishing there with you some day."

"Not at the cost of progress," replied Rick.

Frank jumped back into the conversation, hating to be left out. "I can't believe how much those Indians are bitching. Do you realize that they are trying to change the name of the Redskins? They claim that the name of the football team is demeaning. Have you ever heard such nonsense? If anything, it's a way of showing that the team is good at fighting and being brave, values that Indians are supposed to support." He shook his head angrily.

"Really, Gramps?" asked Nora. "Would you like it if Notre Dame was the Notre Dame Stumbling Drunkards instead of the Fighting Irish? If the San Jose Sharks were called the San Jose Spear Chuckers? And the Notre Dame mascot was the typical stereotype, the drunken Irishman? Or the San Jose mascot was a little black man with a spear? That is what the Indians are complaining about. Calling sports teams by Indian names is racist and mocks their heritage. We would not tolerate this happening with any other racial group, but it is okay with the Indians."

Both Rick and Frank shook their heads. "Sean, my boy, you've been quiet. What are you thinking about?" asked Rick.

"Dad, I just don't get it. I can't wait to graduate. It seems like everyone is a victim. The blacks are victims of slavery. The Indians are victims because white people took their land, which they weren't using properly anyway. The Muslims are victims of the post–September 11 hysteria. The Jews are the victims of the Holocaust. Everyone is a victim, and that means they don't have to work. Well, the Irish were discriminated against, and we made it. We didn't cry victim and ask for all kinds of help from the government. Why can't they just get over it and work?" Sean shook his head. "There are scholarships for blacks, Indians, Muslims. If you are a victim, you can get a free ride to college. But not me. I'm going to have to work, just like Tommy and Nora. These immigrants are taking away all of our chances to get ahead. Those Asians get into any school they want. It just isn't fair."

Pat tried, once again, to educate her youngest. "Sean, these groups have been hurt by our country's actions. Yes, slavery ended in 1865, but laws kept black people in subservient positions until the 1960s. There is so much racism in society. Sure, 100 or 150 years ago there was racism against the Irish and the Lithuanians. But you couldn't tell just by looking at them that someone was Irish or Lithuanian. With people of color, that color is the first thing most people see. They make a judgment about that person based only on the color of their skin. You've never had to deal with that. That is why we owe these people." Pat knew she wasn't getting through to her son just by the look on his face.

"I just don't know why they can't be Americans like the rest of us," Sean replied belligerently. "I agree with Gramps and Gran. They need to adopt our culture and learn to speak English. There shouldn't be special benefits just because they're different."

"Right, Sean," jeered Nora, "become American. Let me ask this—what does that mean? Baseball, hot dogs, and apple pie? You don't like any of that. What makes a person American? What is American culture? Once you get past being born here, being racist, and Christian, and money grubbing, what makes an American?"

"What are you talking about—racist and money grubbing? Being American is believing in democracy, freedom, and equality. That is what our culture is all about. Heroes like Lincoln, Washington, FDR. They are symbols of America and representatives of American culture. They are

Americans." Sean looked at his sister, shaking his head. "And Christian? We let people practice any religion in this country."

Nora shot back, "Let's see: democracy. Well, Washington believed only white men with property should vote, Lincoln didn't want black men to vote, and FDR tried to pack the Supreme Court. Freedom: what does that mean? The freedom to enslave blacks, kill Indians, or the freedom to force your child into a marriage whether they want it or not? Equality: isn't that what the people of color want? When blacks only constitute 13 percent of our population but more than 60 percent of our prisoners, is that equality? When cops target people based on the color of their skin, is that equality? When women make seventy cents for every dollar a man makes, is that equality? Freedom of religion? Name me one national holiday that is based on a religion that is not Christian. Christmas and Easter are national holidays, but not Hanukah or Ramadan. Get a grip, Sean. Democracy, freedom, and equality are meaningless words that politicians throw around to make us feel good about being Americans. They have nothing to do with American culture. American culture is about superiority, money, and racism. And the government isn't doing its job. The government is reinforcing that culture instead of trying to change it."

"That's enough, young lady!" bellowed Frank. "I'll have you know that I fought against Hitler to defend freedom, democracy, and equality. You don't know how good we have it here. Those foreigners and those damned hippies that are in the schools have warped your mind. This is the greatest country on earth, and you should be proud to be an American."

"I am proud, Gramps," replied Nora calmly. "But I do think there are problems in this country, and we need to face them. Those foreigners that you complain about have some solutions for us. What about this: You and Gran are getting old. When you can't take care of yourselves anymore, what are you going to do? Are you going to go into a nursing home or live with Mom and Dad?"

"We're not going into no nursing home, I'll tell you that right off! Those places are torture chambers. We'll live with your mom and dad." Pat blanched at the thought of what her life would be like with these two living in her house. "But what does that have to do with foreigners?" asked Gramps suspiciously.

"Only the fact that the discussion is even taking place," replied Tommy smoothly. "In immigrant families, there would be no discussion. It would be natural that the family takes care of its own. But in most American households, there is a great deal of discussion. We don't want to take care of our elderly. And I think if you were honest with yourself, you wouldn't be comfortable living with Mom and Dad. Like the rest of us, you've become such an individualist that you're not willing to make the compromises necessary to live in an extended family home. That is something we could learn from the immigrants."

"You may be right, but we're not going to have dinner until you kids start telling me what you think is good about this country. Today is the Fourth of July, our Independence Day. I think we should think about the reasons this is a great country," Lila said emphatically.

"All right. Nora, you're ignoring the positive aspects of American culture," Tommy spoke up. "Our huge middle class is a product of our culture. Our standard of living is one of the highest in the world. Foreigners are amazed at how well our poor live. We are able to work and change our social status. In most of the world social status is hereditary, but not here. Here the son of an alcoholic single mother can become president. Although we still have problems with racism, we've done more than any other country to solve the problems of diversity and equality. We don't have religious wars, and we give all religions equality under the law. You're right, Nora, we don't have non-Christian national holidays, but we do give Muslims, Jews, Buddhists, and any others freedom to practice their religion. Most other countries are just starting to do that."

"And what about our educational system?" asked Pat. "While it is true that all three of you have to work to pay for college, in many countries you wouldn't be able to go to college, just because you were born in the lower middle class. Your dad and I have done our best, but there is no way we could pay for three kids to go to college, not after all the medical bills. And that's another thing: our medical care is some of the best in the world. True, we have to pay a lot of money for it, but in lots of other countries, if you're not from the right social class, you don't even have access to good medical care. If we were living in India, your dad would be dead, not here having dinner with us. And don't tell me about social-ized medicine—in Britain and Canada people are dying while waiting for simple operations. The profit motive in medicine means that our medical system has developed all kinds of new, life-saving procedures."

Rick looked at his wife thoughtfully. "Think about our value system. Freedom, democracy, and equality. Nora sneered at them before. But they are good values that guide our country's actions. I know you kids don't agree with some of the foreign policy decisions our government has made, but when you look at history, our country has been very re-strained with foreign intervention. We generally don't try to impose our belief system on other countries. We don't have colonies, and we do get involved in wars to help our friends, like World War I. It is true that we've made mistakes, but we at least admit to them and try to avoid repeating them."

"We're inventive," ventured Sean. "Think about the computer and how it has revolutionized the world. The Internet. Americans are always looking for a better way to do something. We have all kinds of inventions to make life better."

Nora was simmering in anger. "But for all of those good things, there are bad things. Yes, we're inventive, but we're also a disposable society. Capitalism means that the world is intertwined with us. While Dad's right that we don't have colonies, like Britain did, we do have economic colonies. Because we think we're so great, we try to interfere with other countries and their natural development. I know we're supposed to see the good things about our country, but I see problems with everything you're saying."

"But that is a positive also, Nora," said Sean. "Do you think you could publicly make criticisms like this if you were living in China? You would be in jail going through reeducation. And the rest of us would be un-der suspicion. Dad would be dead because the medical care he needed wouldn't be available there. You're right that capitalism means that the world is tied to us, but that means that we help people in other countries.

Because of us there are fewer people starving to death or dying from malnutrition. Since World War II, we've made it a national policy to step in and try to stop genocide in numerous countries. I know you think that we're doing that solely because that would allow us to sell them goods, but the bottom line is they're alive."

The entire family looked at Nora, waiting for something positive from her. Nora closed her eyes, took a deep breath, and said, "Charity. We are a giving nation. We donate to charities, volunteer to help people, and give when it is needed. Yes, Sean, I think that businesses do it so that they can get more customers, but common people, people like us, do all kinds of things for charity, simply because that is part of our national culture. I do think that is a positive part of our culture."

Frank was shaking his head. His mind was whirling around, thinking about the issues his grandchildren had raised. How can they be so critical of this great country? he asked himself.

Lila came back into the room. "Enough of this, everyone. Dinner is served."

They all walked to the table, sat, and said grace.

Points to Ponder

Agree or disagree with the following statements, and give your reasons:

1. Racism in this country will die out as the older generation dies off.

2. Tommy is right: the Mexican immigrants today are no different from the Irish 150 years ago.

3. Nora is right: we need immigrants to do the dirty work so that we can maintain our standard of living.

4. Cultural norms should be taken into consideration during criminal trials.

5. Given what we've done to them, the Indians should continue to get special benefits from our government.

6. In this country, skin color is still the first thing on which you are judged.

7. Sean may sound harsh, but he has a good point. America is becoming a society of victims. No one wants to take responsibility for their own problems.

8. Nora's definition of American culture is too simplistic.

9. Tommy and Nora are right that our society benefits from immigrant cultural values.

10. Indian mascots or names of sports teams that feature Indians are racist and should be changed.

11. This is still a predominantly Christian country, and freedom of religion is not real. School districts do not recognize the right of Jewish or Muslim students to take time off for their holidays, and the government does not recognize non-Christian holidays. Therefore, we do not practice tolerance and freedom of religion.

12. Frank is right: the government is not doing its job properly, particularly when it comes to distributing benefits.

13. The government should enforce a uniform culture taught in the schools.

14. Although there are negatives to American culture, the positives outweigh the negatives.

15. We can have a national culture while allowing immigrants to retain their values.

Essay Questions

1. In most countries political socialization is openly endorsed, uncontroversial, and seen as a social good that helps unite the country. That is not the case in the United States. Discuss the reasons for this, whether you see it as good or bad, and what could or should be done to, if not achieve a more uniform national culture, at least rid our culture of its more negative elements.

2. Discuss the problems of assimilating immigrants. How can we ensure that they uphold our positive social values and not our negative

ones, while at the same time incorporating their positive social values? What role should government have in disseminating culture?

Chapter 7

Smoke-Filled and Other Rooms: Interest Groups

Senator, are you sure you want to do this?" asked Pat Daniels, aide to Senator Diane Keim. "Do you really think that having all of these groups meet together is a good idea?"

"I know it's unconventional, Pat, but my schedule is packed, and I need to see all of them about the same thing. It will be a little tense, but I can handle it," replied the senator confidently. "Actually, it is also an experiment. I'm thinking about a bill to reform interest group activity, to respond to the criticisms made about interest groups. I think if we passed a reform that politicians could only talk to representatives of an interest group if representatives of the opposing interest groups were there at the same time, we could dramatically improve the system. We could get the groups together in the beginning, before the bills were written, and get the compromises out of the way first. Then things would go more rapidly in Congress. We would also stop some bad bills before they even start."

"But Senator, what about the First Amendment?" asked Pat. "Wouldn't that type of bill violate the First Amendment?"

"Not really," replied the senator. "We've passed other bills limiting the interactions of lobbyists and politicians. This would simply be a further limitation. It might work."

"What about the fact that some interest groups do not have opposing groups? For example, there aren't any groups that I know of opposing AARP," asked Pat.

"That's a good point. You know, maybe, with guaranteed access such as that which would result from this change, we would get more interest groups. Realistically, right now an organization that doesn't have a strong interest group doesn't have much motivation to get involved in politics. They probably think they could never get a hearing. This might actually stimulate more interest groups. If nothing else, even if it doesn't streamline the lawmaking process, I do think it would remove some of the appearance of impropriety," said the senator confidently.

"The 'appearance of impropriety' is not the problem. Money is the problem. Access is not going to matter as long as some interest groups are wealthier than others," muttered Pat under her breath, thinking of some of the various scenes she had witnessed while working in Congress. "All right, Senator. I'll set it up for this afternoon, when you get back from lunch," replied Pat, shaking her head. Sometimes members of Congress were just so naïve.

"Good," nodded Diane, "they'll complain about the short notice, but they're all here in town, so it should work. I've got to get off to the meeting now. I'll see you after lunch."

When the senator returned from lunch, she walked into an office that seemed like an armed camp. The aides and assistants were staring intently at their computers while two groups of people glared at one another across the room. They all began talking as soon as she walked in. She smiled and said, "All right, everyone, let's take this into my inner office so my staff can get some work done." She kept walking through the office, and the others followed her.

"Now, before everyone starts complaining, let me say hello and explain myself," began Diane. "Next week the Senate will vote on the new Industrial Standards Bill. As all of your groups have been bombarding my office with phone calls, requesting a chance to have a say, I thought it would be most efficient if we could all meet at once. I know this is irregular, but it is the only way I could fit you all into my schedule. Now, do you all know one another?"

Two of the women shook their heads. Diane made the introductions. "This is Joanne Williams and Isabelle Ruiz from MOAN, Mothers and Others Aid Nature. Joanne, Isabelle, the men on your right are Manny Tree and Rocky Jordan, from Land Lovers, and over here are Jonah Jeffers, from the Autoworkers of America, and Roy Aldman, from the Machine Shop Workers Union. Everybody, please shake hands and be civil." After the introductions were made, the lobbyists began to seat themselves, the environmentalists clustering together and the unionists sitting next to one another. Diane took a seat in the middle of the group and began. "All right, I know you all have strong feelings on this issue, and I know your groups all supported me in the last election. I'll be frank with you, I haven't decided yet how I'm going to vote on this bill. I do want to hear from each of you, mainly on the costs and benefits of the bill. But please, try to be civil here. I know that feelings run high on issues like this, and I don't want Pat to have to call security to stop a fight in my office. That won't do any of our causes any good."

While she was talking, she watched the lobbyists, squirming in their seats, ready to start arguing. As soon as she finished, Roy Aldman spoke up. "Senator, I have to say, speaking for myself, I feel a little outnumbered. You have four environmental lobbyists against Jonah and me. That indicates to me that you've already made up your mind." Jonah nodded his head.

"Not at all, Roy," replied the senator smoothly, "it's just that you and Jonah are the sole lobbyists for your groups. The Land Lovers and MOAN both employ at least two lobbyists to present their case. And, based on experience, knowing you and Jonah, I would say the cards are stacked in your favor—you guys definitely know how to make a point." The joke relaxed the tension in the group a little, but the union men still looked wary. She continued, "If it will make you feel better, why don't you and Jonah go first? Tell me what your concerns are with this bill."

Roy leaned back, took a deep breath, and spoke. "Senator, I'm not against the environment; I like trees, rivers, and blue sky. However, this bill puts too many restrictions on business. The Industrial Standards Bill mandates a 25 percent reduction in all pollutants from all businesses. This is too extreme. Some businesses are creating a great deal of harm to the environment, but others are already very clean. Studies show that it costs more to clean up the last 5 percent of pollution than it does to clean up the first 95 percent. For example, if I'm a CEO of a new power plant, one that is environmentally friendly, first of all, I don't have as much pollution as a power plant that has been in business for fifty years. But we're both supposed to reduce pollution by 25 percent. It is much more difficult and costly for the new power plant to reduce emissions. The older plant will most likely just close rather than implement so many changes. Costs will go up and jobs will be lost. We do need to protect the environment, but we also need to keep people in mind."

Rocky Jordan jumped in as soon as Roy finished speaking. "If you had your way, the only time our kids saw trees or rivers would be in a museum. The people that lose their jobs at your polluting factories can be put to work cleaning up the environment. You just keep producing more and more cars or machines, and they just keep adding to the pollution in this country."

Jonah shook his head. "I suppose you want to get rid of all the cars, all the machines, and go back to living in caves?"

Rocky flung back, "Wouldn't be such a bad idea. Some of you guys haven't evolved from the caveman mentality, so you should go back to your natural habitat."

"That's enough!" the senator said firmly. "Let's keep this civil. You're not doing anything to help me make this decision. Isabelle, your group has always struck me as more moderate than the Land Lovers. What are your feelings on this bill?"

"We support it wholeheartedly, Senator," replied Isabelle Ruiz. "It is a compromise. Businesses will be affected, and people like me will have to pay more for the end product. However, it does cut down on the pollutants that are emitted from industry, and I don't think it is asking too much that automobile manufacturers make their product more fuel efficient. I grant you, we, like the Land Lovers, would like to see more restrictions on industry, particularly more emphasis put on electric alternatives to gasoline, but this is a bill we can live with."

"Aren't you afraid for your husband's job?" asked the senator.

"Yes, we've discussed that. Miguel has little seniority at the plant. With these new regulations he would most likely lose his job. But we both agree that he will look for other work. We would like our kids to live in a healthy environment." Isabelle's voice trailed off at the end, seeing the glare from Roy and Jonah.

"Ma'am, I'm not surprised that your group supports this bill, as your lawyers wrote it." Jonah looked at the shocked faces, particularly Isabelle's. "Yes, that's the truth. Senator Kendall did not write this bill. I was in his office yesterday trying to get him to see the harm this bill would do, even though he introduced it. I have a friend in that office who saw the lawyers from MOAN bringing the original bill into the office and overheard the discussions. Basically, Kendall wouldn't have won reelection without the support of MOAN, and the lawyers flat-out told Kendall to introduce the bill or lose support in the next election. But that is not the point. Ms. Ruiz, do you think your husband will be able to find a job when there will be at least 20,000 people in our state out of work because of this bill?"

"How did you come up with that number, Jonah?" asked Senator Keim.

"From the congressional liaison office. Their figures show that at least 20,000 people in our state will lose their jobs if this bill passes. Nationally, the figure is closer to a half million. Our state will be particularly hard hit, due to all the manufacturing there. This is not something that has gotten too much press, Senator, as there is so much support for this bill on the part of the environmentalists." Jonah looked at the representatives from Land Lovers as he said this.

"Just a minute, I find that difficult to believe. If that were the case, the media would be all over it. Still . . . ," said Senator Keim. She used the intercom to get Pat's attention. "Pat, call the liaison office for me. Find out their figures on the projected loss of jobs if this bill passes, and let me know." Turning back to the lobbyists, she said, "Jonah, I understand the bill includes funds to retrain people who have lost their jobs. Isn't that enough?"

"No, Senator," Roy answered instead. "The jobs that will be lost are union jobs. These jobs include strong benefits and protections. Unfortunately, the new jobs will not be union jobs. They will pay less, there will be fewer benefits, and fewer protections for workers. Ms. Ruiz's husband will probably end up making less than half of what he now makes." Ms. Ruiz visibly blanched. She began to look nervously at her checkbook.

"And then he won't be able to buy one of those brand new cars that you keep rolling off the assembly line!" Manny Tree glared at the union men. "Senator, you need to understand that in the past five years the number of trees in our state has declined by one-third due to disease, 600 miles of river are so polluted that they cannot sustain life, and the air pollution is getting worse. This affects all people, not just in our state, not just in the United States. Pollution from our factories causes acid rain in Canada, and toxins from our rivers eventually flow into the oceans. We need to dramatically cut back on the amount of pollution we create. We need to restore wetlands to help the environment recover. This bill is just a palliative. We need to start closing down factories and turning to environmentally friendly means of production and transportation."

"That's right," Roy shook his head, "ducks are more important than people. We need more wetlands for the ducks."

"Mr. Union Man, we need wetlands, but not just for the ducks. Wetlands are nature's filtration system. If we rebuild the wetlands, they will filter out most of the pollutants that go down the rivers into our oceans. That helps bring the rivers back to life also. Don't you ever want to take your kids fishing?" asked Manny.

Before Roy could answer, Rocky jumped in. "Jonah, you're concerned about the loss of jobs for autoworkers. Don't you think the companies would employ more of them if they were forced to develop electric-powered or biodiesel-powered cars? Instead of one assembly line for each model of car, you would have numerous assembly lines for electric cars and biodiesel cars. Wouldn't that actually create jobs?"

Joanne jumped into the fray. "And those workers that lose their jobs in industry. Why not train them to produce antipollution technology? Right now we're not producing it because there isn't much of a market for it. The Japanese are leading in that industry because we haven't seen any need to develop such technology. But Americans are some of the most inventive people on earth. Shouldn't we devote some of our people and resources to developing this technology? Maybe we could fund this new development through an additional tax on gas."

"You're damn right American workers are the most inventive people on earth!" replied Roy. "But you've got to understand, these things don't happen overnight. Businesses take years to bring new models into production. If we're just starting on developing antipollution technology or alternative-fuel cars, it will be at least ten to twenty years before these things go into mass production. That is an entire generation of workers who have lost their means of livelihood. I understand your concerns, Ms. Williams. Do you understand mine? Many of my union members will not benefit from this in any way. Sure, their grandchildren might live in a cleaner environment, but will they even be able to afford to have children, let alone grandchildren? They need to support themselves today and not in an industry that hasn't even begun to develop. And increasing the gas tax would actually hurt the country. A gas tax is regressive; it affects the poor more than the wealthy. If the poor have to pay more for gas, then they have less money to spend on other products and the economy suffers. By the way, you should know about the Japanese efforts in this area. Doesn't your husband work for their lobbying agency? And didn't you work for the EPA in the last administration?"

"Yes, that's true. But what's the problem with any of my family's current or former associations?" asked Joanne.

"Just the fact that I don't like spokespeople for foreign governments making our policies. And the fact that you used to work for the EPA means that you can call on your old friends there to paint this bill in the best light possible for Congress when hearings are held. Hell, we saw that already. The EPA is totally in support of this bill and won't even acknowledge there are any problems." Roy shook his head in disgust.

"Man, that is the kind of thinking that has gotten us into this mess," groaned Rocky. "We just keep putting off making changes, and one day it will be too late, if it isn't already."

"Listen, young man," Jonah said quietly, "I admire your dedication. But you need to live in the real world. If we go to alternative fuels, then the Middle East becomes even more destabilized. The oil-producing countries will lose their main source of revenue. With their high birthrates, that will leave a huge proportion of the population with no jobs. That spells social unrest and war. None of us benefits from that. Likewise, if we adopt these new standards, our products will be more expensive, not only here but abroad as well. We will then sell less abroad, business revenues will decline, and people here will get laid off. We need to change in a rational manner, not irresponsibly."

"But we've been behaving irresponsibly for generations. Our country produces more pollution, uses more resources than any other country in the world. If we went to alternative fuels for cars, you're right, it wouldn't happen overnight. The oil-producing countries would have time to develop new businesses to employ their people. It would be in their interest to diversify their economies. That would help you in the long run, because it would create more customers. You want me to live in the real world. Okay." Rocky paused for a breath. "I understand that the economy is global, that what happens in the Middle East affects business here. Do you understand that what we do with the environment affects the world? We can change the way the world treats the environment by changing the way we do things here."

"If that were the way it would work, I'd support your views wholeheartedly," replied Roy. Rocky dropped his glass of water in surprise. "Unfortunately, that's not the way it would work. Businesses in this country would simply move to other countries in the world where environmental restrictions were not as strict. It would actually make the problem worse. Senator, that is one of the things I wanted to bring up to you. I would like an amendment to this bill giving tax breaks to companies who kept their production facilities here, abiding by the new regulations. This might help keep companies from relocating their plants elsewhere."

"You know, Mr. Manufacturer, I would have more sympathy for your view if it all wasn't a big con game," interjected Manny, laughing at the confused look on the faces of the union men. "Get real. The businesses in this country are not interested in the good of the country. If they were, they would focus on making reliable products."

"What in the hell are you talking about? Has your mind deteriorated from spending too much time in the wilderness?" asked Roy.

"Just this," replied Manny. "Businesses in this country make products with a limited lifetime, so the consumer will have to buy replacements. This keeps businesses profitable. My old man has to buy a new VCR every year. You can't tell me that these things are not designed to break after a given period of time. And it's no different in other industries. We make things that are disposable, and that keeps businesses making money. It also contributes to all the problems we have with the environment. If businesses made reliable products, they would eventually run out of customers in this country. So they sell overseas, but the price doesn't go down. Why not make reliable products and reduce the price? Then more people could buy them. Eventually you will get to the point where everyone owns as much as they want, but then you could just invent something new. We need to stop this disposable-society mentality that we have."

Roy shook his head. "You don't realize that machines are not perfect. They will break. You can't make something that lasts forever. And aren't you also a part-time lobbyist for a Canadian environmental group? Just like Joanne, you're speaking for a foreign government's interest rather than ours."

"I'm speaking for our interest. Canada is affected by our pollution. I also am not dumb when it comes to machinery. I know machines are not perfect, but you can't tell me that we haven't found a better way of making VCRs. They've been making them for more than twenty years. I don't believe that we haven't found a way to make a VCR that lasts more than a year." Manny looked at Roy smugly.

Roy continued shaking his head. "You really need to come down to earth. No company would intentionally make something that breaks. It just isn't good business practice."

Manny just laughed.

The Senator nodded her head. "I've got to say, Roy, that Manny has a point. I, too, find myself replacing my VCR regularly. And my microwave oven, even my telephone. We do have a disposable society, and I think our businesses could do a better job by making products more reliable. At the same time, we need to keep our businesses healthy, so that they can continue to pay taxes to support social programs. I don't know if reliability is something we can legislate, though. It seems to me that the public needs to raise this issue with businesses, and businesses need to respond to it."

"Senator," asked Rocky, "why don't you think we can legislate this? If a business is making a dangerous product, the government gets involved. If a business is involved in fraud, the government gets involved. Isn't this the same thing? If a business makes a product that it knows has a very limited life and doesn't tell the consumer, isn't that fraud?"

Roy snorted in disgust. The senator smiled at Rocky and said, "How do you know it is deliberate? How could that be proved? Businesses could argue that it is just the natural life of a machine, that there is nothing they can do to make it last longer. I for one can't argue with that, because I don't know enough about the engineering that goes into making the machines. Theoretically, we could hire engineers in the government to evaluate the products and see if there is any way to make them last longer, but that would lead to a dramatic increase in the size of the federal bureaucracy. I don't know if that is the best way to go about doing things."

"Something is better than nothing, Senator," replied Manny. "This would give businesses an incentive to change their ways."

The senator smiled at the two men. "I'd like to get back to the bill. But just a minute . . . Yes, Pat. Really? Thanks." She turned to the lobbyists. She took a deep breath. "Jonah, your numbers are wrong. The revised estimate is that 50,000 people in our state would lose their jobs, and close to a million would lose their jobs nationally." She shook her head. "I don't know. You've all brought up good points. I agree that we must do something for the environment. But I don't know if I can support a bill that costs so many jobs. I'll need to consider everyone's points. Thank you all for coming. I appreciate the information you've given me."

"Senator, keep in mind," said Joanne, "you're running for reelection next year. If you want our support, we do expect you to vote the right way on this bill."

Senator Keim glared at Joanne. "I realize that your group supported me in the last election. But so did the other groups here. I can't please all of you. I need to think about this. At least some of you will be disappointed with my vote. Right now I don't know who it will be. But this is a decision I will make. You all did your jobs by giving me information on the pros and cons of this bill. And yes, Roy, I will consider an amendment encouraging businesses to stay in this country rather than going elsewhere. Good day, everyone."

The lobbyists filed out of the room, still divided into groups as they had been at the beginning of the meeting. Pat stuck her head in the office and asked, "Senator, do you have time to speak to Representative Goody?"

"Sure, Pat, show him in," replied the senator.

"Hi, Diane," said Lucas Goody. "I want to talk to you about cosponsoring a bill. I just got out of a meeting with George and the guys from Citizens for Ethics in Government. We were talking about the problems associated with interest group influence."

"Great! I've been thinking about interest group reform myself," said Diane enthusiastically. "What type of changes were you discussing? You'll love what I've come up with."

"Well, you know how the media is killing us on living arrangements. After it broke that six members of Congress were living above the Fellowship Church at greatly reduced rent, the media has been looking for other instances of this type of influence. They just don't understand how expensive it is for most of us to live here in D.C. and maintain a home in our constituency. Now keep in mind we were discussing this over a liquid lunch, and it sounds a little bizarre, but hear me out. There is a navy base in Virginia that is going to be closed down, as part of the peace dividend. It has housing, a commissary, a laundry, everything a small town would have. Why don't we turn it into congressional housing? Members of Congress could live there either rent free or at a reduced rent, it would be easier to secure than all of us living all around the district, and it would make a lot of sense. Not only would it eliminate interest-group housing subsidies for some members, it would eliminate a lot of members of Congress socializing with lobbyists. I mean, I'm not going to have a group of lobbyists or even a single lobbyist come to dinner if I'm living on a closed base with other members of Congress.

"Realistically, we could get work done there, at least informally, and maybe even carpool or have buses to take us back and forth to the Capitol. Think how that would help the D.C. traffic problem. And it would reduce smog and free up all kinds of parking in the district. It would also enable some people to run for office who can't now because they can't afford to live here and have a home in their constituency. What do you think? I realize there are problems with it, but I think we could explore the idea."

"Really, Lucas . . . ," Diane's voice trailed off as Lucas interrupted her.

"It would also cut down on the morals problem. It would be much more difficult for members to have affairs if we're all living on this base—What? Why are you looking at me like that?"

"Lucas, you're serious about this, aren't you? I thought maybe this was just the result of too much liquid at lunch, but you're really serious," said Diane somberly.

"Yes, I'm serious. I think this could have great benefits for the country. What's your objection?" asked Lucas abruptly.

"Well, first of all, it would be a prime target for terrorists. But most of all, there is no way I want to live that close to other members. I like to get away from them. Now, let me tell you my idea." And Diane, not seeing the look of reproach on the representative's face, proceeded to outline her reform, explaining how helpful it was to have representatives from competing interest groups debate the issues for her.

Points to Ponder

Agree or disagree with the following statements, and give your reasons.

1. Interest groups have too much power and too much access. None of the interest groups here are really representative of mainstream society.

2. The problem with interest groups is that they are looking out for their interests, not the interests of the country.

3. Politicians pay too much attention to interest groups.

4. Interest groups need to talk to one another more often.

5. We cannot put the environment ahead of jobs in this country.

6. Too many interest groups are too extreme. Both unions and the Land Lovers advocate policies that would drive business out of this country.

7. Interest groups are no longer grassroots organizations. They have paid lobbyists, staff, and PR people, and this has caused them to just become part of the system rather than representatives of the people the groups were created to serve.

8. Interest groups perform an important function by educating politicians about laws and regulations that would impact their members. Therefore, we need more interest groups.

9. Unions in this country have gotten too strong. They have won increased wages and benefits for their members, but in doing so they have cut the profits of corporations. Therefore, corporations are leaving the country to find cheaper workers elsewhere. Our economy would benefit from weaker unions.

10. Manny is right. Businesses in our country make products that are designed to break. This keeps the market going.

11. The media sometimes does not present all aspects of a proposed bill, in order to gain support for that bill.

12. Regulation is the best way to force companies to make better products. Vigilance has been left to the consumer for too long, and nothing has changed.

13. Interest groups taint the process, making politicians obligated to them. We should amend the Constitution to get rid of interest groups or at least prevent them from donating money to politicians.

14. We need to implement policies to increase the number of interest groups in this country, so that there is an interest group opposing the AARP, for example. Too many interest groups are so strong that no one is willing to oppose them.

15. We should explore limitations on interest group activity, as Diane proposes. This would be a beneficial reform.

16. It is wrong that an interest group writes a bill for a member of Congress to introduce. There is an inherent conflict when this happens.

17. It is wrong that foreigners or Americans can advocate policies that benefit foreign governments.

18. Too many interest groups are able to blackmail members of Congress like Senator Keim. We need to change the system.

Essay Questions

1. Discuss the pros and cons of interest group activity in this country. What changes would you make to eliminate corruption while preserving the rights of the people to influence government?

2. Our Founders felt interest groups were the best protection we had for minority rights, seeing interest groups as part of checks and balances. Are interest groups today still fulfilling that role? Why or why not? What changes would you implement to improve the system?

Chapter 8

A Dime's Worth of Difference?:
Political Parties

This is BBC World News Roundup. From London, I'm Cyril Lloyd-Jones with a special edition focusing on the primary elections in America.

"The American political establishment is in shock this evening with the results of the primary election in the state of Kentucky. In an electrifying upset, political newcomer Samuel Farman has defeated three-term incumbent Senator Tom Goodwin for the Republican nomination for senator by a vote of 65 percent to 30 percent, with 90 percent of the vote counted. Farman will run against Democrat Joan Cloud, an American Indian, in the general election in November. Ms. Cloud beat Juan Muñoz in a hotly contested Democratic Party primary. Mr. Muñoz is a former Brown Beret, a group that militantly advocates immigrant rights. His strong showing illustrates the growing power of the Hispanic vote in America. Mr. Muñoz was leading in his primary race until the media broadcast videotape of him entering a hotel room with a married woman. Although Mr. Muñoz is not married, the fact that his lover was married caused dissension among his supporters and most likely cost him the nomination.

"The race is controversial because of Mr. Farman. Not only is he a political novice, his personal background is, to say the least, unconventional. In his teenage years, he was a Socialist Party member. He later rejected socialism and joined a New Age religious group, the Rock of Ages. Rockers, as they are called, worship nature, particularly meteors, which they say are celestial signs of the oneness of man with nature. Mr. Farman was arrested and imprisoned for five years for trafficking in narcotics. He appealed his conviction on religious grounds, arguing that his religion mandated the use of narcotics to worship. That appeal was denied, but a later appeal on entrapment was upheld, and Mr. Farman was released after spending eighteen months in prison. His civil rights were restored when his conviction was overturned, enabling him to run for office. While incarcerated, Mr. Farman became a member of the Aryan Brotherhood, a white-supremacist group that is particularly strong in America's prisons. He was a member of the Aryan Brotherhood for more than ten years, formally renouncing his membership the day he filed his papers as a candidate for the Senate. In the clip that follows, Samuel Farman attempts to explain his somewhat unconventional path to mainstream politics.

"I realize that many people might think I'm flaky, at best. However, like so many of my fellow citizens, I grew up during a time of tremendous turmoil in this country. The violence of the civil rights movement, the antiwar demonstrations, and the political assassinations of the sixties all caused me to question our system and look for alternatives. I am not condoning socialism, the Rockers, or the Aryan Brotherhood. I have, in fact, rejected all these organizations. When I was growing up, the mainstream political parties and mainstream culture did not offer solutions to the problems I saw in society. Today, however, the Republican Party does offer answers. Their rejection of homosexuality and interracial dating and marriage, and their emphasis on family values and individual initiative, I feel, provide the solutions I was looking for as a youth.

"Needless to say," continued Cyril, "The Republican Party is not enthusiastic about Mr. Farman's candidacy. They do not like being favorably compared with such organizations as the Rockers or the Aryan Brotherhood. However, in America, political parties have no control over the candidates. Unlike Britain, where the parties choose the candidates, in America the candidates are self-selected. Anyone can run under any party label, as long as they meet the minimum qualifications and can pay the filing fee, which varies from state to state but is not expensive.

"Mr. Farman's winning of the nomination is difficult to explain. Most analysts felt that the incumbent, Senator Goodwin, would win renomination easily. However, it appears that the voters in Kentucky are punishing Senator Goodwin for defecting from the party over the issue of contraception. Senator Goodwin led the opposition to the Republican-sponsored bill that would have outlawed any federal money being used to pay for contraception for children under eighteen. Senator Goodwin said, 'While I encourage my children to practice abstinence, I would prefer that they had access to low-cost birth control if they decide to become sexually active.' Mr. Farman was a vocal supporter of the bill, and it looks like the Republicans of Kentucky agreed with him. It must be remembered that American political parties cannot control their members. Here in Britain, a member of Parliament must vote with the party. In America, that is not the case. Nor are American politicians bound by the will of the voters. Even though Senator Goodwin knew his constituents supported the ban on contraceptive funding, he felt free to vote as he saw fit, disregarding the wishes of his constituency. He now appears to be paying the price for voting his conscience.

"It also appears the voters are punishing him for poor parenting skills. Senator Goodwin's oldest son has had several problems relating to his use of illegal drugs and underage drinking. Joshua Goodwin, seventeen years old, has been arrested three times, twice for underage drinking and once for illegal drug use. He is currently awaiting trial for violating his probation by drinking again. It is likely he will face stiff punishment. Senator Goodwin aroused resentment when he asked the media to respect his son's privacy. The media had extensively covered Joshua Goodwin's court appearances, arguing that the public had a right to know what actions the senator would take in regard to his son. For example, if the senator pleaded with the court for leniency, it would indicate he expected a dual standard of the laws, one for his son and one for everyone else. In spite of the media's argument, the coverage of Joshua Goodwin's troubles is not sitting well with many Americans, who are of the opinion that the boy needs to be able to get his life back on track in private. The fact that Mr. Farman made Joshua Goodwin's problems a campaign issue might also explain his win. In spite of what they said in public opinion surveys, it seems most Kentuckians agreed with Mr. Farman's question to Senator Goodwin: 'If you can't raise your son to respect the law, how can we expect you to make decisions for our state and our nation?'

"The Republican Party now faces a quandary. Mr. Farman is an embarrassment to the national party and to many in the Kentucky Republican Party. At both levels, party officials can disavow Mr. Farman and refuse him party support. However, that is not politically expedient. Kentucky's incumbent governor, George Scott Pierce, a Republican, is also running for reelection. His opponent is Democrat Karen Gold, former secretary of the interior. That race is extremely close, with polls showing both candidates at 40 percent of the vote, with 20 percent undecided. Governor Pierce needs as much help as the Republican Party can give. In addition to national elected officials campaigning for him, the governor would like financial support from the state party. And therein lies the problem for the Kentucky Republican Party. If they want to give money to help reelect the governor, that money will also help to elect Mr. Farman. The national party is limited in how much help it can directly give to Governor Pierce's campaign. However, the use of so-called 'soft money' is different at the state level. Soft money is money that goes to help the party overall. It would fund commercials encouraging people to 'Vote Republican,' voter education materials, registration drives, and other party work. While this soft money would help the governor, it must be nonspecific, not targeted to any single candidate. Thus, Mr. Farman would also greatly benefit from the expenditure of soft money in the state.

"Mr. Farman's campaign and winning of the primary election has renewed calls for political party reform in the United States. Joining me earlier in the day via satellite was Professor Jessica Scholl, author of *Reformed to Death: American Political Parties.* She had this to say," and Cyril turned to face Professor Scholl on the monitor.

"Well, Cyril, Sam Farman's candidacy is the logical outcome of what we have done to the system. One hundred years ago political parties in the United States were much stronger, similar to your parties in Britain. However, in response to corruption, the system was reformed at the beginning of the twentieth century. More power was given to the citizens to choose candidates. Further reforms after the problems of the 1960s led to widespread adoption of the primary election as a means of choosing candidates. The political parties became weaker and less ideological. Today we have liberal Republicans and conservative Democrats, and there is really no meaningful difference between the two parties. In part this is a reflection of the homogeneity of America, with its huge middle class. We could never have class-based political parties as you do in Britain. The Republicans and Democrats agree on most substantive issues. Thus our disagreements tend to focus on whether or not the government should regulate something, whereas your parties disagree on the form of government, form of the economy, and other fundamentals. We do not. But I've gotten away from my point.

"With all of these reforms, political parties in America have become too weak. They have no say in the choice of candidates, no ability to discipline errant members, and little control of party ideology. In a very real sense, we have no opposition party, regardless of who controls the government. For example, in Britain, the Labour Party is currently in control of the government, with the Tories in opposition. It would be unthinkable for a member of the Labour Party to lead the opposition to a Labour-sponsored bill. That is the job of the Tories. That, in essence, is a functional democracy. However, in America, it is normal for a party member to lead the opposition to a bill supported by his or her own president and party, as we saw in the case with Senator Goodwin. Our parties do not have a strong ideological base and therefore do not perform the functions of opposition parties.

"It is not just the Democrats today that are not functioning as an opposition party. In 1992, when Clinton won the presidency and the Democrats controlled the Senate, the Republicans did not function as a true opposition party. To some extent, after the 1994 midterm elections, when the Republicans gained control of the Senate, they did function as a true opposition party. Their 'Contract with America' was a strong ideological criticism of Clinton's programs. However, this only happened because the Far Right dominated the Republican Party at that time, with Newt Gingrich as Speaker of the House. During that period, the majority of Americans were not happy with the government. Because of the strong ideology of representatives like Gingrich, the government was forced to shut down twice. Given this experience, most Americans would prefer that their parties were not strongly ideological. In part, it's because Gingrich represented the Far Right. I think if the Republicans had not been so far right, more Americans would have seen the benefits of true opposition.

"Today, the third parties are the only real opposition. It seems to me that we need to return to the early twentieth century and give the parties back some of their power. The ability to decide on candidates would be a good place to start. This would eliminate incidents like Mr. Farman's candidacy. It would also help the public. They would know what a candidate stands for just by seeing the party label. You would no longer have to wonder if this was a liberal or conservative Democrat. We would probably need a third party for those liberal Republicans and conservative Democrats, but that too would be good for the country. And with so many social services having been assumed by the government, political parties no longer have the opportunity to use patronage, and thus much of the basis for the past corruption would disappear."

Cyril's thoughtful face filled the screen. "Wouldn't this type of reform create more problems in your system? With your weak parties, the two main parties can incorporate popular third-party ideas. If you went to more ideologically based parties, wouldn't you end up with more parties and more fracturing of your very diverse society? After all, your weak parties increase social cohesion, bringing disparate groups together."

Jessica Scholl nodded. "Yes, there would be more parties initially. But I am hopeful that once Americans became accustomed to the benefits of strong ideological parties, they would coalesce around a few ideologies. Essentially, Cyril, at this time the only function political parties serve is to provide labels for candidates and a means of organizing committees in Congress. Today we have Sam Farman as a Republican in the same party with Representative John Rush, who supports government funding of abortions, greater regulation of business, and affirmative action. These two men are far apart on the political spectrum, but they both belong to the same political party. Not only does it not make sense from the standpoint of the political scientist, it also creates more divisions in our society. The followers of these two men do not have anything in common but a label. This does not unify our country. Strong, ideologically based parties would force Americans to come together and work through our differences."

"While that might be true," observed Cyril, "it has not worked that way in other countries. Here in Britain, for example, strong ideologically based parties have actually worked to polarize the country. We have seen class identification strengthen and even some class-based riots. Aren't you worried that might happen in your country also?"

"No, because our country is so strongly middle class," replied Jessica. "Your parties are ideologically strong, but they evolved out of class-based parties. That is not the case here in America. We have the welfare mother agreeing with the corporate tycoon on many issues. There are welfare mothers and members of the working poor who have a conservative philosophy. They don't like big government, they want less regulation, and they don't like the idea of sexual promiscuity. Likewise, liberalism has a broad base in all of the economic classes. There could be strong ideological parties in America without the problems associated with class that you have in Britain."

"But Professor Scholl, as I understand your political system, those most active in your parties are those in the extremes. For example, the religious right in the Republican Party and those advocating socialist programs and extreme environmentalism in the Democratic Party. These are the people most likely to be active in their parties and to vote in the primary elections. Am I correct?" asked Cyril. Jessica Scholl nodded.

"Well," continued Cyril, "wouldn't giving more control to the parties exacerbate the problem? Wouldn't you then continue to get even more extreme candidates? Realistically, if the Democratic Party were in control of the selection of candidates, they would not have selected Joan Cloud. She's a moderate when it comes to social programs like welfare, and she opposes socialized medicine. Although she is an environmentalist, she's not a supporter of the radical environmentalists in the Democratic Party. Juan Muñoz, however, does support those programs. Isn't that so?"

"Well, you're right, Cyril," responded Jessica grudgingly. "However, I do think that stronger parties are the answer. It is possible that at first we would have extremist candidates. But I think with time the American people would gravitate toward parties in the center, and the extremist candidates would not win elections."

Cyril nodded and then asked, "Would more states consider adopting Louisiana's policy? Correct me if I'm wrong, but doesn't Louisiana delay the primary until the day of the general election, allowing the incumbent to run against all of the opposing candidates?"

"Yes, Cyril, that is what Louisiana does. However, that gives a greater advantage to incumbents. They generally do not face opposition from within their own party, and therefore it becomes difficult for the voters within the party to change candidates. Also, the election must be won by at least 50 percent or there will be a runoff election. This leads to uncertainty. I'm not sure that is in the best interest of the country. Thank you, Cyril, for letting me have my say, but now my time is up."

Cyril's somber face reappeared on the screen. "As you can see, there is disagreement about the best way to reform the American political system. You may have noticed that Professor Scholl advocated greater party control over the choice of candidates but pointed out that the problem with Louisiana is the incumbent is less likely to be challenged from within the party. It would seem that some of the reformers themselves have not thought through the implications of their reforms. We now hear from Charles Stedham-Jones, of Oxford University, resident expert on American politics. Thank you for joining us again, Charles."

"Thank you for having me, Cyril."

"Please give us your reaction to the American primaries and the reforms proposed by Professor Scholl," asked Cyril, smiling.

"Cyril, the American system is much different from ours. While Professor Scholl is correct that their parties are weaker than ours and their society is predominantly middle class, the reforms she is advocating are not enough. Those reforms would not solve some of the basic problems in their system. For example, the way Americans finance campaigns is influenced by the First Amendment to their Constitution. One of the peculiarities of American politics is the fact that anyone can create a campaign advertisement in support of a candidate. In the senate race you were discussing, the racist organization the Ku Klux Klan paid for and developed commercials in support of Mr. Farman's campaign. Mr. Farman wanted nothing to do with these advertisements, but the First Amendment allowed the Klan to run their own commercials in support of Mr. Farman's candidacy. The Klan also held numerous rallies in support of Mr. Farman. Something like that would not happen here in Britain. That is only one of the significant differences in our systems. Thus, just going to more ideological parties will not fundamentally change American politics," Charles said.

"That is a good point. But surely that is the exception, not the rule in American politics," said Cyril thoughtfully.

"Unfortunately, that is not the case," observed Charles. "In the primary election in Wisconsin, an interest group called Citizens for Ethical Politicians ran numerous commercials encouraging voters to choose Jack Strong. The commercials endorsed Strong because his opponent, Carol Lynch, had been arrested for child abuse. That was the extent of the commercial's message. What the commercial did not say was that Ms. Lynch had been accused of child abuse, but the charges were almost immediately dismissed. The child who made the accusation had serious mental problems and could not offer any support for her accusations. According to the child the abuse took place over the two-week period immediately before the arrest. However, Ms. Lynch was not even in the country at the time of the alleged abuse. The commercial gave none of this information. Ms. Lynch lost the primary, mainly because instead of addressing the issues raised by the campaign, she was forced to spend her time refuting the allegations of child abuse. Problems like this won't be solved unless the Americans are willing to dramatically revise the First Amendment, something that is unlikely," said Charles, shaking his head.

"I see. What are the other problems that you see in American party politics?" asked Cyril.

"Well, federalism is a problem. Essentially, the Republican Party is not one political party, it is thousands of political parties. There are state Republican parties in each of the fifty states, and there are many local Republican parties in each state. In one sense, these numerous parties are a strength; they act as transmission belts, exchanging ideas from the national to the local level. Thus, if the national party decides that the right to abortion is not a value they wish to support, it can transmit that idea to all of the state and local affiliates. However, there is no guarantee that the state or local party will support the idea. Likewise, if there is a new idea at the local level, like school vouchers, then the party machinery can transmit that idea to the state and national level. While this is a strength, it is also a problem. The First Amendment guarantees freedom of association, so the national Republican Party cannot discipline local affiliates that disagree with the national party. To stay with the example of abortion, there are local Republican Party organizations in California that vehemently disagree with the national party. These local organizations support a woman's right to choose and flout the party line. There is little the national organization can do to pull the locals into compliance. Thus you get candidates like Sam Farman. They are reflective of the local conditions, but anathema to the national party organization." Charles heaved a heavy sigh, rolling his eyes at the stupidity of the Americans.

"But isn't that simply a means of allowing the largest number of people in a very diverse society to participate in the political process?" asked Cyril.

"Yes, that is the intent. However, as Professor Scholl correctly pointed out, this does not unify the country. Fundamentally, the parties are still in the hands of rich white men. The Democratic Party did take measures in the 1970s to diversify, ensuring a certain percentage of the seats at the national convention for women and people of color, and that has been somewhat successful in diversifying leadership positions. The Republican

Party has been less successful. Unfortunately, as we have seen in our own country, the impression is that people who receive these seats are not qualified or have not paid their dues by working in the party for a long time. As I said, the Democratic Party has been more successful in diversifying than the Republican Party. Ron Brown, a black man, was the chair of the Democratic Party while Clinton was president. Brown was seen as qualified, but there is still resentment at the perception of quotas. The Republicans have reacted to this perception by mostly keeping power in the hands of white men. There are some women in high positions in the party, but these are positions without much power, reflecting the Republicans' conservative views on the proper position of women in society." Charles paused to take a drink of water.

"So, their political parties have some of the same problems we have with diversity. What could they learn from us and our experience?" asked the anchor.

"Well, the fact that Clinton was not the chair of the Democratic Party while he was president is laughable to us. Realistically, he could want one thing while the party advocated another. This would never happen in our system. With our strong party system, the prime minister is the leader of his or her party. Thatcher was able to become prime minister not because of any diversity program, but because she worked within the party, demonstrated her talent, and convinced other members of the party that she had an ideology that would help the country. When the country voted for the Tories, they knew that if the Tories won the election Thatcher would be our prime minister. In America, the public can vote overwhelmingly for Republican candidates but still elect a Democrat as president. While this is part of the American system's checks and balances, it makes for strange election results and difficult party politics."

"So you wouldn't advocate that the Republican Party adopt diversity programs? Shouldn't they do as Tony Blair did and ask for more representative candidates?" Cyril looked confused.

"The Republican Party is in a quandary. The Democratic Party has traditionally been the party of diversity. However, American society is changing. There are more people of color who disagree with the Democrats on fundamental issues like affirmative action, premarital sex, abortion, family values, and many other issues. People like Clarence Thomas, the Supreme Court justice, and Colin Powell, former secretary of state, have strong conservative ideas. However, for most people of color with conservative ideas, the Republican Party is not seen as welcoming. They see this party as the party of segregation and hostility to the idea that racism is still a problem in society. The Mexican American segment of the population is the fastest-growing minority. Because Mexican Americans are people of color, most Americans would assume that they would become Democrats. However, Mexican Americans are also predominantly Catholic. While it is true that most Catholics are Democrats, because of that party's historic tolerance for diversity, among the Mexican American population the ideology is much closer to Republican Party beliefs. However, the Republican Party does not seem to be trying to reach Mexican Americans. It seems as though the Republicans are assuming that Mexican Americans will just naturally gravitate toward the Republican Party. But it is not happening. The Republican Party needs to reach out to these people, but it can't fundamentally change its conservative message. This is not an easy path to walk. It would help if Republican leaders would at least admit that segregation was wrong and racism is still a problem in America. This would not necessarily be an endorsement of affirmative action, but an acknowledgment of the realities of American life."

"Do you see any of these changes taking place in American politics in the near future?" Cyril gave Charles a chance to recap his main points.

"No, I don't think the Americans see these issues as major problems, so there won't be any change in the near future. American politics promises to continue to be interesting for the observer." Charles smiled at the camera.

Cyril concluded with, "So, the turbulent game of American politics is as rough-and-tumble as ever. We will keep you apprised of further developments. This is Cyril Lloyd-Jones for the BBC."

Points to Ponder

Agree or disagree with the following statements, and give your reasons:

1. It is almost impossible to tell the difference between Republicans and Democrats today.

2. Political parties should be able to control their choice of candidates.

3. Political parties should be able to discipline members who do not adhere to the party line.

4. Jessica Scholl is wrong—too much power is still in the hands of the political parties. Giving them more power would just make a bad situation worse.

5. Political parties should be able to use soft money to help individual candidates.

6. Money in politics is part of the problem and should be banned.

7. Politicians' families should be covered by the media. Joshua's problems help the voters understand the political choices his father will make. If nothing else, knowing that the senator has a child with a drug problem would indicate how the senator might vote on drug-related issues.

8. Giving control back to the parties would mean fewer people of color and women as candidates.

9. We need a strong third party not just to represent the moderates, but also to force the Republicans and Democrats to address other issues.

10. The American public is undereducated about politics and unwilling to learn about the candidates. Therefore, they should not be the ones to choose the candidates.

11. Giving power back to the parties would just give more power to rich white men who don't have the best interests of women and people of color at heart.

12. Louisiana's way of combining the primary with the general election

╴ᴗᴜ. This allows the voters to have a greater impact and cuts down on the long campaigns.

13. Third parties are the only true opposition parties today.

14. We need to revise the First Amendment to prevent interest groups and candidates from producing misleading or false advertising.

15. We should think about adopting some of Britain's policies, like having the president be the leader of the majority party in Congress. This would simplify elections by eliminating the Electoral College and also ensure that the will of the majority is represented.

16. The Republican Party should adopt diversity programs so that people of color and women are better represented in decision-making bodies.

17. Cyril is wrong when he claims it is a problem that the president is not head of the party. Federalism and ideological diversity are a fundamental part of the checks and balances of our system.

Essay Questions

1. Political parties serve many functions in this country. What recommendations would you make to change the system to better reflect the needs of our country and our government?

2. The Founders did not envision political parties, and George Washington advised against them. Were the founders right or wrong in their opposition to political parties?

Chapter 9

Selling Candidates: Campaigns and Elections

All right, class, settle down. As there are no more questions on this topic, I would like to try something a little different. We are going to have a discussion. The ground rules: nothing said in this room leaves the room; no shouting; no calling names; you will listen to each other respectfully, and then respond politely if you disagree. Can we all agree to these ground rules?" The students all nodded, some laughing at Professor David Wiley. "Okay, we'll start with something simple—how many of you are going to vote next month?"

Less than half the class raised their hands. Wiley shook his head. "Well, you are all old enough to vote, and you are all citizens. Why aren't the rest of you going to vote?" Numerous voices began speaking. "One at a time. Janie, why aren't you going to vote?"

"Well, David, really, at first I was kinda excited about voting, but now I'm just bored with it. The campaign has been going on sooo long. I just tune it all out now." Seeing the expression on her professor's face, she rapidly went on, "I know voting is important, you've taught us that, but the campaign just never seems to end."

"Janie made a good point. Our campaigns are some of the longest in

the world. Members of the House are almost always on campaign; senators and potential presidents begin campaigning two years before the
election. Americans as a whole have short attention spans. Should we reform the system? In Britain, campaigns are limited to one month. Would
that be something that we could do here? Justin, what do you think?"

"Well, man, I agree with Janie that the campaigns are too long—but
one month, what can you really learn about the candidates? I mean, this
year we've got the president, a senator, a member of the House, a governor, and state and local legislators. How could we get enough information in a month? Too short. We need more time."

Amy snorted at Justin, saying, "Get real. There is a reason for the
long campaign, particularly for president. I grant you two years is a long
time, but that tells me the candidate is serious about wanting the job
and healthy enough to survive the pressure of being president. Shorten-
ing the campaign means that we could get a president who isn't healthy
enough to serve for the four years."

Before the professor could reply, Norman jumped into the discussion.
"It's not just that one month is too short. We need better information. I
mean, really, if you rely on the mainstream media, you just get the party
line, no real news. If you do research, you can see how the candidates
voted in the past, see what they've said in speeches, really get to know
their positions. But that is difficult with so many candidates. We need
some kind of unbiased, easily accessible source for information. Then
maybe a month would be long enough."

"All right," Professor Wiley said. "One of the major problems is adequate information. Would you be willing to spend some taxpayer dollars
to fund a nonbiased information source that would collate information
on each candidate and be easily accessible?" There was a chorus of agreement. "Billy, you're shaking your head no. What is wrong with this idea?"
Several of the class members groaned. They knew Billy too well.

"Well, Professor Wiley, I just think it's impossible for the government
to present unbiased information. They're going to present things in a
way they want us to hear. Can you really believe the government would
give an accurate portrayal of third-party candidates, like the Socialists or

Greens? I mean, the government wants to retain their monopoly on power; they're just going to do everything possible to ensure that Democrats and Republicans—who are no different from each other—stay in office. It is all part of the conspiracy. . . . " Billy was cut off from developing his usual theme.

"While I disagree with your conspiracy theory, Billy, as I've often mentioned on your papers, let's focus on one point of yours—the two-party system. One reason the electoral system in Britain works well is stronger parties and more of them. You don't really need to research each candidate; if you know what the party stands for, you know how each candidate will vote. That is not likely to happen here. But you're right that our system is controlled by two parties. Would more of you be encouraged to vote if there were more viable parties?" Professor Wiley wanted to draw the discussion away from Billy's conspiracy theories.

"Yes, but . . . " Wiley looked at Anita with surprise. While an intelligent young woman who always did excellent work on her assignments, she had never once spoken up in class. "But what, Anita?" the professor asked.

"What about the Electoral College? Isn't it set up for a two-party system? If we want strong, viable third parties, we would have to abolish or radically alter the Electoral College." There were cheers from the class, many of whom still did not fully understand the Electoral College, despite numerous lectures on it. Anita continued, "I agree that stronger third parties would be good, but I don't think I want to give up the Electoral College for them." Now there were boos. Anita began to retreat into her shell.

Professor Wiley immediately glared at the class. "I thought we had agreed that we would all listen respectfully!" The class quieted down. "Anita, go on. Not too many people today defend the Electoral College, particularly after the 2000 election. I'm curious as to why you want to keep it."

Anita smiled. "I have to honestly say I voted for Gore and was disappointed with the way the Supreme Court handed the election to Bush. But we shouldn't throw the baby out with the bathwater. The Electoral

College is a strong component of federalism. Without it, presidential candidates have no incentive to pay attention to the rural populations, the populations of the smaller states. Keep in mind: Bush defied conventional wisdom by concentrating on the smaller states. The Electoral College ensures that the president is representative of all of the people." Professor Wiley smiled as some of the other students grew thoughtful. "You make some valid points, Anita. What about the fact that votes in the Electoral College are not equally weighted? By this I mean that one elector in a state like California represents roughly 615,000 popular votes, while one elector in a state like Wyoming represents maybe 164,000 popular votes. Isn't that inherently unfair?"

"No," replied Anita. "Not in my opinion. No one ever said life or politics should be fair. There are inequities all of the time. The popular vote is solely to choose electors. There is no mandate that they represent equal numbers of popular voters. As in so much related to American government, there are trade-offs. To have a president representative of the country as a whole, each elector carries equal voting power. The Founders knew that some electors would represent a larger popular vote than other electors and felt it was an acceptable way to choose our leader. I have no disagreement with that."

"What about the rest of you? Do you think we should abolish the Electoral College or even modify it? Is this what is stopping so many Americans from voting? Adam, you wrote a scathing criticism of the Electoral College on your last exam. What do you think—that is, if you even know what we're talking about?" Professor Wiley was always irritated when students drifted off to sleep or read during his classes.

Adam looked up as if not seeing Professor Wiley but slowly replied, "Yes, I know what you're talking about. You're right; I hated the Electoral College on the last exam. I felt it was an outmoded, ridiculous way to choose our leader. But I hadn't considered Anita's points. It is important for the candidates to pay attention to the entire country, not just focus on the population centers. And that is what would happen if we just went to the popular vote. My uncle lives in Wyoming. They have a lot of problems there with the EPA, the National Park Service, and other federal bureaucracies. Their congressional delegation is not strong enough to fight the contingent from, say, California. With the Electoral College, the presidential candidates at least have to listen to the people of Wyoming. So, I guess maybe we should keep the Electoral College, but maybe modify it in some way."

"How about proportional representation? You told us about how they have that in some other country; I can't remember which one, but maybe that would work with the Electoral College. . . . " Tim started to feel silly because he hadn't fully thought out his statement.

David Wiley nodded. "Good thought, Tim. You'll be surprised to know that you're not the first to consider it. What some have suggested is that in each congressional district the vote be tallied, and the candidate who gets the majority of the popular vote in that district would get that Electoral College vote. The two statewide votes, corresponding to the number of senators, would go to the highest vote getter in the state. This would also strengthen third parties, which tend to be regional. Someone did a study of this. I'm sorry that I don't remember the exact details, but the result was something like out of the last fifteen presidential elections, thirteen would have resulted in no candidate getting a majority and the election being thrown into the House of Representatives. The proposal didn't get much attention after that."

"Um, David . . . ," Freddy began. "Yes, Freddy?" asked the professor.

"Well, if the Electoral College is intended to ensure that the president is a representative of all of the people, why don't we ensure that he has to build a national coalition? By this I mean get away from the simple majority in the Electoral College and go to a supermajority. I think it would be better if the candidate had to win at least two-thirds or maybe even three-quarters of the Electoral College vote to become president. That would make it less likely that we would have a president winning the majority in the Electoral College but losing the popular vote. It would also ensure that the vast majority of the people voted for the president."

David looked at Freddy thoughtfully. "You have a good point there. Usually a president represents the majority of city dwellers, for example, and barely pays attention to rural voters. A supermajority would ensure that the candidate really responded to the nation as a whole. However, we would probably have more elections thrown into the House of Representatives, as politicians couldn't get that supermajority."

"At first, you're probably right," replied Freddy. "But eventually we would get candidates that actually tried to focus on the country as a whole, instead of regions as we do now. And, just looking at the table in the back of the textbook, between 1964 and 1996, only in two elections, in 1968 and 1976, has the winner not received at least a two-thirds majority in the Electoral College. In fact Clinton only received a two-thirds majority. In the other elections from 1964 to 1988 the winner won by more than a three-fourths majority except for 1968 and 1976." Many of the students looked thoughtful.

"Mr. Wiley . . . "

"Yes, Jesse?" "Can we change the subject a little? I mean, I know the Electoral College is important, but really, that's not why I don't vote. For me, it's the selling of the candidates. I really get so disgusted with the way these guys raise money. It just seems like the candidate who sells out to the highest bidder wins."

"Okay, class, Jesse has a point here. Do we need campaign finance reform? If so, what kind of reform?"

At this the entire class fell silent. They remembered the extensive lectures on this topic. Nate, who was not one of the more imaginative students in the class, asked, "How do other countries handle this problem? What can we learn from them?"

"Good question," replied the professor. "Going back to Britain, one thing to keep in mind is, with only a one-month campaign, costs are much lower. Also, in Britain there is a ban on advertising in the media. The government sponsors a few debates, but all other advertising must be done on a person-to-person basis, going from door to door and handing out information. Contributions are given to the party, not to the candidates. Would that work here? Another option that some countries use is complete government funding of campaigns through tax dollars. That way you don't have wealthy individuals or corporations influencing the campaign. What do you think? This also does away with all of those negative ads you hate so much." There were general murmurs of agreement. None of the students liked the current funding of campaigns. Almost anything sounded like an improvement. Then Anita raised her hand. Professor Wiley nodded at her. "What about the First Amendment, Professor? Didn't the Supreme Court rule that private individuals could spend their own money to support a candidate? That this was constitutionally protected free speech?"

David Wiley smiled inwardly. The discussion was really bringing Anita out of her shell. If nothing else, this was a valuable result of this use of class time. "Anita is right. The Supreme Court did rule as she says. This type of reform would entail an amendment to the Constitution. Thank you, Anita, for paying attention." Anita blushed. David looked at Jessica, who was almost falling out of her chair.

"Well, personally, I would support a constitutional amendment that would ban all campaign advertising. Candidates, interest groups, private parties would all be banned from advertising. I grant you, we would get more stunts by candidates to get news coverage, but I do think it would eliminate a lot of problems." Jessica stopped to take a breath, while some members of the class grumbled. "I mean, really, that would get rid of the negative campaigning, it would stop politicians from trying to expose every part of an opponent's life, it would just make everything easier. I think we would also get more candidates, because they wouldn't have to raise so much money."

Before anyone could respond, Billy jumped in. "But then the only information we would get would be from the media, which is corrupt and part of the conspiracy . . ."

"That's enough on that topic, Billy," David said sternly. "Jessica raises some valid points."

Brian raised his hand. David smiled at him, and Brian said, "I like Jessica's idea, but I also want some restrictions on the media. I really don't want to know everything there is to know about a candidate's personal life. I mean, I realize that if a candidate comes out for family values and is having an extramarital affair, the media should report that. But I don't like the fact that they analyze everything you ever did. Really, how many of you could handle the media investigating every aspect of your life? This is costing us good candidates, people who could serve this country but don't want their entire lives splashed all over the media."

David nodded and then replied, "But where would you draw the line? What would be acceptable? For example, with George W. Bush, many people felt his possible drug use in college was important, if nothing else because it would show a double standard. He was able to avoid any trouble but supported strong antidrug laws. Is that something you feel should be covered or not?"

"Honestly, David, I don't know," Brian said, troubled. "All I know is that I don't like all of this personal stuff on each candidate. I know that if I wanted to run for office, there are mistakes I made that I wouldn't want the media to cover. Not that I broke any laws, but I've done some stupid things. Maybe just a ten-year limit. If it happened more than ten years before, the media leaves it alone."

"So," Jack interrupted, "twelve years ago you got away with a hit-and-run. The public doesn't need to know about that? Of course, that would be criminal and part of the public record. So, fifteen years ago you got a girl pregnant and left her high and dry. Never acknowledged the kid, let alone paid child support. Shouldn't the media show us what kind of a person you are?"

Brian looked thoughtful, as if he hadn't considered these issues.

Nina said, "I would like the media to be responsible. What I mean is I want a report card on each candidate. Compare their campaign promises to what they actually did while in office. Obviously, sometimes they won't be able to live up to their promises, and we could ask them to explain why not. But this way, at least they won't just say anything to get elected." The class murmured in agreement.

José raised his hand. David nodded to him. "I find it interesting that we're talking about the president being the representative of all the people and discussing taxpayer funding of campaigns. That just doesn't relate to reality for me. All month the president has been flying around the country in Air Force One, at taxpayers' expense, campaigning for himself and members of his party. It just doesn't seem right to me," José said emphatically.

Professor Wiley nodded, "José has a good point. The president is running for reelection and helping campaign for others in his party. However, you'll notice that he always has at least a semblance of official business on these trips."

"Now, yes," replied José, "but two years ago it was simply campaigning for others in his party during the midterm elections. I'm sorry, but I think that is partisan politics at the taxpayers' expense, and I feel that is wrong."

"Good point, José," replied David Wiley. Before he could say anything else, another student jumped in.

"David, can I say something?" asked Ivan. The professor nodded and Ivan continued, "While everyone has made good points about the length of the campaigns, the Electoral College, and campaign finance, that is not the real problem I see. I just read James Bryce's book, *The American Commonwealth*. His argument is that the American system is geared to find a winning candidate, not the best leader. Think about it. The campaign is essentially a long job interview. I know a lot of people who are really intelligent and would do good jobs, but they can't get the jobs because they don't interview well. There are also people who interview well, but can't do the job at all. Just think about some of the new professors here, not naming any names, but we've all had a certain economics professor who obviously impressed the interview committee but can't teach worth a darn. I think that's one of the problems here. Some of the people who would do a fantastic job as president can't cut it on the campaign trail. Part of it is they can't raise the funds, but part of it is they don't look good in the media or are too intelligent for the American public."

The class looked at Ivan in awe. Most of them had never considered the campaign in that way. Others were thinking of some of the job interviews they had been on, unsuccessfully. Professor Wiley asked, "Assuming you're right, Ivan, what would you recommend?"

"Well, you're not going to like it, but go back to party control. Rather than let anyone run for president, let the parties choose the candidates *without* input from the public. The parties will choose candidates who are qualified and have the experience and ability to lead the country. We could then choose from those candidates." The class snickered, many students shaking their heads. One student, hiding in the back of the room, called out, "What about democracy?"

David Wiley glared at the back of the room. "Who says we're living in a democracy? The Constitution says nothing about democracy. Actually, Ivan is right in one respect: that is how we get the vice presidential candidates. At least, it used to be. Now the candidates for president choose their own running mates, without any input from the public. What do you think?"

"Well," said Rita, "I don't know if I like the idea of giving the power back to the party. But I do think we should either make the vice presidential candidate the one who came in second in the primaries or have a whole set of primaries for the vice president. Considering the vice president is just a heartbeat away from the presidency, we should have some say." The class nodded in agreement. Then a voice from the back of the room called out, "*Survivor!*"

David looked around, unable to identify the student. "Okay, whoever it is, I warned you to take this seriously. I think this is a valuable way for you to learn, but if you don't take it seriously, I'll just go back to lecturing."

Paul, in the back of the room, cleared his throat. "I *was* being serious. Honestly. I read an article about a country in South America, I think it was Argentina, where they have a *Survivor*-type show to choose a candidate. It is not for president, but from what I understand, it is similar to our congressional district elections. Essentially, all of the contenders from one political party appear on the show. Journalists ask them questions, and at the end of each night, the audience votes someone off the show. The one left at the end is the candidate. We could do something like that here. It would mean we get to know the candidates better, without their PR people. They would be on the spot, having to answer questions, and the public could vote them off the show by dialing a telephone number." David looked disgusted, but many of the students nodded in approval.

"Well, I suppose that is one way to get candidates and the public more involved in politics, but I have to say I personally hate those *Survivor*-type shows," said David.

"Let's move on—actually, back to where we started," he continued. "As you know, political scientists have been worried about low voter turnout for some time. They have raised various proposals to increase voter turnout. The major suggestions are mandatory voting, a national holiday on election day, a twenty-four-hour voting day, easier registration, and voting entirely by mail. What do you think? Would any of these proposals encourage you to vote?"

Tim jumped right in. "I like the idea of a national holiday. I work in construction, and even though the polls here are open from 7 a.m. to 8 p.m., I can't always get from my job to the polls to vote. I know I could vote by absentee ballot, but I'm always afraid that something will happen after I mail in the ballot, and I won't be able to change my vote. The twenty-four-hour idea is okay, but would we be able to find people to work at the polls that long?"

"It can be done," replied Wiley. "Keep in mind that would eliminate the media jumping the gun. If all of the polls closed at the same time, you wouldn't have the media predicting the winner when people on the West Coast and in Hawaii and Alaska are still voting."

Several of the students nodded in agreement. George added, "We need easier registration. I moved last week, and it is too late to register in my new address. If I want to vote, it either has to be absentee or I have to drive over a hundred miles. Realistically, it is not going to happen. I should be able to register at the polls."

Other students nodded in agreement, but Anita shook her head. David looked at her, and she said, "So you want to trade off convenience for fraud? In parts of this country, particularly in some areas of Illinois, dead people still vote on a regular basis. With relaxed registration requirements, fraud will be easier." George looked abashed. Anita went on, "I'm curious about mandatory voting. What exactly does that mean?"

Professor Wiley explained, "In some countries, like Italy, you are required to vote. If you don't vote you not only face a large fine, but also your identity papers are stamped 'nonvoter.' While we don't have identity papers in this country, at least not yet, what some have suggested is putting nonvoters' names on billboards or in the newspapers. This would shame people into voting. Good idea or bad?" David looked around and saw another of his traditionally mute students ready to jump out of his chair. "Simon?"

"Do we really want that? I mean, I know some people who don't pay any attention to politics. If we had mandatory voting, rather than face the fine—these people really don't care about public humiliation—they would go into the booth and just punch holes anywhere. This wouldn't be informed voting. I would rather have low voter turnouts with informed voting than people just voting so as not to be fined. . . . " Simon's voice trailed off, as if he couldn't believe he had actually spoken in front of so many people.

Once again, David nodded his approval. "Simon has identified the major problem with mandatory voting. It doesn't guarantee that the voter will be responsible. Yes, Joan?"

"Well, David, why not have mandatory voting, but include a box that says 'I choose not to vote'? This would get people into the voting booths, and if enough people are choosing not to vote, maybe the system would change, maybe we'd get better candidates. If nothing else, we could get money for social programs."

"What do you mean?" asked David.

"If people don't vote, then they have to pay a fine, right?" David nodded. Joan continued, "Well, the money from the fines can go to things like homeless shelters or college scholarships. I mean, if we make it like a speeding ticket where penalties add up if you don't pay it, we're talking some major money. And, so that we don't have to hire a bunch of people to track down the nonvoters and collect the money, why don't we do something like, if your organization volunteers to collect the money they get to keep it. I mean, there are a lot of people who would go and collect the money to support their favorite charity."

Dwayne shook his head. "Do you know how much corruption there would be in that type of system? I mean really. If I owed money for not voting and you came to my door to collect, I wouldn't believe you. I'd think you were going to keep the money yourself. No way would I give you the money, no offense."

"Maybe . . . ," started Jill. David nodded to her. ". . . Maybe instead of having the volunteers collect the money, when you pay your fine you could stipulate where the money should go, which program you support. And then you would also start getting these people involved in politics, because they would see that they do have impact on programs. If nothing else, the money from the fines could go to voter information and education programs for nonvoters. There would still be the problems of bureaucracy, but with computers there wouldn't be too much actual work." Several students nodded in agreement.

Frank spoke up. "I find this whole discussion absurd. I'm sorry, but I can't believe people don't vote. It is a responsibility that comes with citizenship in this country. We have a duty to be involved, to have a say in our government. Don't you realize that our forebearers fought a war so that we could choose our leaders? What happened to that sense of responsibility in this country? Yes, it is difficult. We have to research and make time to vote, but that is as it should be." Frank shook his head as some of the students looked abashed.

David Wiley smiled. "Unfortunately, our time is up today, but I hope that some of you have changed your minds about not voting. See you next week."

Points to Ponder

Agree or disagree with the following statements, and give your reasons:

1. In recent elections less than half of the qualified voters voted, so we can't still refer to ourselves as a democracy.

2. Low voter turnout is dangerous to this country. We run the risk of the elites gaining even more control of the country and taking rights away from the lower classes.

3. Campaigns in this country are too long, too expensive, and too distracting. The system must be changed.

4. The Electoral College has outlived its usefulness. Our country would be better served by changing the system of selecting a president.

5. The current method of financing campaigns must be changed. Corporations are buying candidates, and the system is rife with corruption.

6. People around the world are fighting and dying for the right to vote, just as people in this country have fought and died for that right. Nonvoters are unpatriotic, almost traitors.

7. The system will not change because it is not in the interest of the Republicans and Democrats to change it. They benefit from the current system, and they control it.

8. It would be impossible to establish an unbiased information bank to help inform voters about candidates and issues.

9. Voting in this country is a palliative. Our votes are really meaningless. Voting is a way to give the people the impression they have power when they really do not.

10. It is wrong for the president to campaign for himself or other members of his party on taxpayer money. The system must be changed to prevent this clearly partisan use of taxpayer money.

11. We should reform the Electoral College so that the candidate must have a supermajority to win.

12. Amy may have a good point about the benefits of the long campaign, but overall the costs are too great. We should limit the presidential campaign to no more than one year. With better medical reporting, we can ensure that a potential president is healthy.

13. The public should help choose the vice president, either by a primary campaign for the office, or by naming the second-highest vote getter in the presidential primary as the vice presidential candidate for that party.

14. We should explore the possibility of mandatory voting, with the fines going to fund social programs. As long as there is a box to check

that says "I choose not to vote" or "None of the above," we wou... the problem of irresponsible voting.

15. While a *Survivor*-type show might not be the best way to choose a president, it might be a good way to get candidates for Congress.

16. Although occasionally we get too much detail, there are valid reasons for the media to explore all aspects of a candidate's life.

Essay Questions

1. Discuss the problems associated with campaigns and elections in this country. How would you change the system to allow it to more fairly and accurately reflect the desires of the people?

2. Many of the Founders felt that only men with property should vote, since they would be the ones having to pay any taxes. Write an essay either agreeing or disagreeing with the point of view that the electorate should be limited to those who are going to pay most of the taxes.

Chapter 10

Shooting the Messenger:
The Media

Well, Peter, are you ready to see our forces at work? You've been here for more than a week interviewing us, seeing how our forces are fighting for liberation, fighting our version of your American War of Independence. Do you want to go along on the next raid?" asked Ani, the interpreter for the Asian Liberation Group.

Peter replied without hesitation, "Yes, I need to see you on a raid. The footage I already have is tremendous, but the American people need to see your forces on a raid. That's the only way I can convince the American people that our government is lying to us, that you are not terrorists but freedom fighters. Much of the footage I already have is persuasive, but I think I should also show your people fighting for their freedom. I can handle the march through the jungle."

"Very good. I promise you that your footage will not be disappointing. We'll leave now." And so the band of guerilla fighters set off on their trek, the American reporter following with his camera, cell phone, and other implements of his trade. Trudging through the jungle, he momentarily regretted the fact that his cameraman had refused to come with him. The footage would be so much more dramatic if he could be seen narrating

133

the images that would be shown back in the United States. However, the fact that the cameraman wouldn't come meant that he would not have to share the glory when his report was shown to the nation. He stumbled over a root in the dark and muttered a curse.

Ani grabbed his arm. "You must be quiet now. We are almost at the objective." Peter nodded, still unsettled by seeing a small woman carrying an Uzi. In spite of his cultural chauvinism, he knew Ani was capable of using the weapon. This war was based on widespread support, and these people knew that women were as essential as men in bringing about change. He was startled when Ani told him they had arrived. Standing on the top of a peak, he looked down at a military base. Surely the rebel band was too small to attack such a fortified base. He panned his camera, catching Ani and her band, heavily armed, and then focused the lens on the base. When the image became clear, he was surprised, but hid his shock. Sami, the leader of the band, spoke to the rest of the guerillas. Ani translated for the camera.

"We will strike in ten minutes. Mortars will be fired from these three hills, aiming for the armory and the barracks. Most of the soldiers will be sleeping, so we will have an opportunity to do a great deal of damage. The explosions in the armory will disorient them. Hoji." The young man nodded his head. "You are responsible for the machine guns. Shoot the soldiers as they attempt to leave the barracks. While your group pins them down, Jin in the camp will set off the explosives in the motor pool and base hospital." With those instructions, the guerillas moved off into position. Peter taped it all, catching extraordinary video of the mortar attacks, explosions, and numerous deaths of the forces opposing the Asian Liberation Group. After a long trek back through the jungle, Peter packed his supplies, made for his jeep, and said a sad goodbye to the guerillas.

Within an hour he was in the city, where he went straight to the airport and boarded a plane back to the United States. After sleeping on the plane, he began to think about the report he would be filing. He could have filed the film from the city, but felt it was better to wait until he returned to the United States. His editors would not be willing to show this film without some argument.

★ ★ ★

"Peter, have you lost your mind?" exclaimed editor John Nuggins after watching the footage Peter brought back from Asia. "The media here is up in arms about the unprovoked terrorist attack on the American base, the attack which claimed the lives of forty American soldiers and caused millions of dollars' worth of damages. The fact that American women personnel died has the entire country polarized. You were there, with the terrorists, and knew at least ten minutes beforehand that they were going to attack the Americans. Don't you think you should have called the base and warned them? Innocent Americans died, for God's sake. What were you thinking? You want to show video of guerrilla women killing American women? I'm sorry, but I can't approve this video myself. We're going to need Mr. Murtock to sit in on this week's story meeting."

Peter shook his head wearily. It was as bad as he thought it would be. Thank God this was a weekly newsmagazine. At least he had some time to argue for his story. He stared at the walls, waiting for Mr. Murtock, the station owner, to arrive. Within minutes the owner joined the group. He watched the tape Peter had brought back with him. John Nuggins recapped his objections for the owner.

Peter immediately started to refute John's arguments. "John, they weren't innocent Americans. You've seen the other footage I shot. The ALG is not a terrorist organization. They are an independence movement, fighting against an oppressive government that has no respect for human rights. Our government is not only supporting that government, but also using our military to help subdue the rebellion. You saw that footage of our military participating in the attack on the rebel base. American soldiers participated in the massacre of children and the rape of Asian women. None of those killed at the rebel base were carrying arms; they were there to be safe from that government's military. As far as I'm concerned, our government is participating in terrorist activities. And American corporations are helping. They've been paying the government there millions of dollars for mineral extraction rights. That money is supposed to go to help increase the standard of living for the common people. Instead it is going right into secret bank accounts for the leaders of the country, mainly President Sunarke. The people are not benefiting. And, big surprise, those same corporations make huge donations to our president and members of Congress responsible for making foreign policy decisions."

"Peter," Sarah, the agency's legal representative, interjected quietly, "it is possible that you will face charges here in America for aiding and abetting the attack on the American base. As an American, you had a duty, moral if not legal, to warn those soldiers. American lives were lost and American interests were hurt."

"I disagree. I am a reporter. I'm supposed to report the news, as it happens. I can't interfere with the story. If I had done anything, I would have become the story. Yes, American lives were lost. Even if I had warned them, American lives would have been lost. But my job is to tell the American people what is happening in Asia, why our troops are there. What I saw was an affront to everything America stands for, and the American people should know what we're doing there." Peter was in full-fledged righteous-anger mode.

"Ahem," Jason Murtock cleared his throat. "Peter, I respect you as a newsman. Let me ask you this—if you had a tip telling you when and where an attempt would be made on the life of the president, would you inform the Secret Service, or would you just be sure that we had a camera crew there? I'm trying to understand your journalistic value system."

"I don't know . . . , honestly, I don't know. It is not that clear-cut. If there were time, I probably would warn the Secret Service. But in this case, it was a judgment call. I had ten minutes. I had seen the horrible treatment that the Americans meted out. I was there to report on the situation. That is what you sent me to do. Let me ask you—if I had called you when I found out that the Americans were the objective of this attack, what would you have done? Knowing that it was possible that if I warned anyone, the rebels might have killed me?"

"I don't know, either," replied the station owner solemnly. "I just know that this does not feel right. My son is in the army. Fortunately he is stationed in Germany. But I would like to think that if one of my reporters had information that Jared's unit was about to be attacked, they would warn him."

"Mr. Murtock, do you think that the *Washington Post* was wrong to pursue the Watergate story?" asked Peter.

"No, obviously not. The *Post* showed that the president was grossly abusing his powers. The American people had a right to know about the wrongdoings of the Nixon White House. Part of our job is to be a check and balance on the government. If we don't inform the American people about government mistakes, the people cannot make informed decisions about their elected leaders."

"I agree," Peter said enthusiastically. "What about Vietnam? Do you think the media did its job in Vietnam?"

"Yes, of course we did. We showed the American people what was happening. We informed them." Murtock was confused by the question; the answer seemed self-evident.

"Mr. Murtock, if you had known beforehand, would you have had a camera crew at My Lai, to record the massacre there? And if so, would you have shown that tape to the American people?" Peter was driving his point home as John and Sarah watched closely.

Murtock thought for a moment and slowly nodded his head. "Yes, I would have recorded the massacre and shown it to the American people. They had a right to know what our soldiers were doing. I see where you're going. I agree that the majority of the footage you shot is strong journalism. You show the excesses of the American troops and the reasons for the insurgency. But I'm still not convinced about the final shots of the attack on the American base."

"Don't you see," replied Peter, "what I was doing in Asia is no different than having a camera crew at My Lai. I was informing the American public about the mistakes made by our military and our leaders. The ALG is a legitimate independence organization. They are fighting against a brutal government that has been imposed by an outside power, and they want to have freedom, democracy, and basic human rights. You saw that in the earlier footage I shot. In no way does the ALG threaten our national interests. As a matter of fact, they are more in accord with our national interests than the government we are supporting. Showing this footage is no different than blowing the lid off of Watergate or My Lai."

"Well, Peter," said John snidely, "it is nice to know that you are better qualified to make foreign policy decisions than the entire Washington establishment."

"That's unfair, John," interjected Sarah. "Media stories constantly present facts that show that the establishment doesn't know what it is doing. Just last week we ran that exposé on the problems in HUD. While I'm not entirely comfortable with what Peter did in this situation, I'm also uncomfortable from a legal standpoint. Morally and ethically, there is little difference between what we did with HUD and what Peter did in Asia."

"What specific legal problems do you see, Sarah?" asked the owner.

"Given the Revised Patriot Act, it is possible that Peter might be arrested as a combatant, just as John Walker Lindh was arrested. He had knowledge of imminent danger to American troops and interests and did nothing to stop that danger. Likewise, this corporation might face some legal problems if we show the footage and support Peter."

Jason Murtock looked at Peter. "Would you be willing to give the government information on the rebel band, where they were based, their armaments, their numbers? I mean, anything that the government couldn't get from watching this footage?"

"No, absolutely not. As far as I'm concerned, they are no different than the other sources we use. Would you be willing to give the government the name of the source at HUD? Of course not. That is a fundamental principle of journalism. If I gave the government information on these people, the military would be there within days to exterminate them."

John shook his head, unable to believe what this reporter was advocating. "You are still trying to say you know more than the entire intelligence establishment about what is best for our country."

"John, we have a duty to the people, not only of America, but of the world as a whole. Think about what recommendations our intelligence establishment has made in the past. Not only the intervention in Vietnam. Think about all of the dictators we have supported, all of the misery we have had a hand in creating. We wonder why so much of the world hates us. This is why. In Asia we are supporting the imperialistic power in a colonization effort opposed by the masses. If we continue, we will create another group of people that hates us. We will help create future terrorists willing to strike out at our country. By showing this tape, maybe we can force the intelligence community to rethink and avoid repeating past mistakes. Isn't that part of our job?"

John looked at Peter. "I'm curious as to your characterization of the ALG as an independence movement. From what I see, including the footage you've brought home, they are a group of terrorists trying to overthrow the legitimate government. By what standards do you classify them as an independence movement?"

Peter sighed again. "John, as you know, Asia was subjected to Western colonization for hundreds of years. There, as in Africa, the European powers drew boundaries that cut across historic divisions, dividing ethnic groups. The ALG is composed of a minority ethnic group in a country governed by their historic enemy. That government is trying to eliminate any trace of the minority culture. The ALG is fighting to maintain their cultural identity against what they see as a foreign oppressor. In my book, that makes the ALG an independence movement, no different from the men who threw the tea into Boston Harbor in the 1770s."

John shook his head.

Sarah nodded in agreement with Peter. But before she could say anything, Mr. Murtock began to speak slowly while gazing off into the distance. "You make some good points, Peter. The media does have a responsibility to the American people to show the mistakes made by our government. That is one of the main reasons the Founders guaranteed a free press. However, it must also be a responsible press. We cannot knowingly show incendiary footage. We have a responsibility to our stockholders as well as to the American people. After Owl News showed that story on Muller, the convicted sex offender living near the grammar school, and after the riots that resulted from the story, we all have to ask ourselves how people will react to our reporting."

"That's what I'm worried about," said Sarah. "Not only could Peter be tried as a combatant, but the corporation could face legal action if we air this story. The soldiers that participated in the raid on the refugee camp could sue us for slander or defamation of character. While the video does show the soldiers acting in ways we see as irresponsible, possibly criminal, they could still sue us. Individual faces are clearly identifiable in the video. Maybe if we blur the faces of the soldiers it would help. I'm fairly confident that we would eventually prevail in court, but this corporation would endure a great deal of negative publicity in the meantime."

Murtock nodded. "That's one of my concerns. But I'm also not sure we should show something so critical of America and our troops while they're fighting a war. As you say, we are supposed to report the news, not make it. I have a responsibility as the CEO of this station to ensure that what we show is in the best interest of the country and the employees of the station. I'm not sure that the stories coming out of Vietnam were best for this country—the way we treated the veterans of that war was unconscionable. I don't want to start that type of coverage here, with this war."

"What about the war here at home, Mr. Murtock?" asked Dan Reason, another reporter, who had been sitting quietly, listening to the exchange.

"Mr. Murtock, Dan has a story that he feels we should run, and I'm not sure about that story, either. All right, Dan, make your argument," Nuggins said wearily.

"Mr. Murtock, there is a serial killer stalking the streets of this city. This killer is waging war on the drug dealers and prostitutes. The police know about it, but don't want it publicized. I understand you've already gotten phone calls from the mayor and the chief of police." Dan waited, and Mr. Murtock nodded his head. Dan continued, "I realize that the police have a point, that they don't want the killer to know they're on to him. However, I've been sitting on this story for two months, just for that reason. In that time, there have been four more killings. We have a duty to the public to let them know what is going on. The police will just have to deal with it when the information gets out there."

Mr. Murtock rubbed his forehead. "Dan, the police assure me they have a suspect. They're just waiting to get enough evidence on him. If we run this story, we could spook the guy, and he would never be caught. We do have a responsibility to the public as a whole here."

"Forgive me, Mr. Murtock," replied Dan respectfully, "but I've been hearing that for two months. Did the chief tell you that these killings appear to have been going on for more than two years? Did he tell you that in spite of the fact that some homicide detectives felt more than eighteen months ago that this was a serial killer, no extra resources were allocated until two months ago, when I asked the chief for comments on the case? And if they have a strong suspect, what was he doing when the last four killings took place?"

Mr. Murtock shook his head. "What are you saying, Dan?"

"Mr. Murtock, you don't seem to understand," said Dan slowly, as if talking to a child. "The victims in this case are all black, and the vast majority of them are criminals of some kind. The chief of police and the mayor are white. They have been heard referring to this killer as a garbage man. They seem to feel he is doing the city a service. Now, if the victims in this case were middle-class white people, there would have been a great deal more police activity before now. Would you believe that the FBI still hasn't been consulted? If the victims were white, the FBI would have been consulted a long time ago. As it is, the only reason that the police have been devoting more manpower is the fact that I've been making some waves."

"Really, Dan," interrupted Nuggins, "you're not that important."

"Maybe not," replied the reporter, "but this station is. The police are worried about bad publicity. And I'm not saying the entire police force is racist; there are some very good cops, both black and white. But the allocation of resources is ridiculous. For example, last month there was the hit-and-run driver that injured Tina Scott, a nice little white girl. There were over twenty police officers devoted to finding the car that hit her. And she lived. However, there have been more than thirty killings of drug dealers and prostitutes in this city in the past two years, and for the majority of them no investigation was performed. Right now, after I've made waves, there are only two detectives on the case full time. There are four others who are called in 'as needed,' provided their other cases don't conflict with investigating this one. I realize that the cops respond to public opinion; that is why there were so many resources devoted to finding the driver who hit Tina Scott. But we can run this story and force the cops to respond to the serial killer. Believe me, the public will care; if no one else, dealers and prostitutes will care."

"Do you have video of all of this?" asked Mr. Murtock abruptly.

"Most of it, sir. I have video of the victims, the detectives, and various aspects of the case. I don't have video of the chief or the mayor referring to the killer as a garbageman, and I wouldn't mention it in my report. But we have a duty to report this. What happens if the next victim is a 'mistake,' someone who is just in the wrong place, someone who is not a dealer or a prostitute? How would you feel then, if we hadn't run the story?" asked Dan.

"I would feel the same way as I would if the next victim was a drug dealer or a prostitute!" exclaimed Mr. Murtock. "We're not arguing the value of one life over another here. What we're discussing is the most socially responsible way to handle this story. We need to be sure, if this story is aired, we don't do irreparable harm to the police investigation. And just as with Peter's story, we have to think about the impact of the story on the public. If we run this story and it leads to race riots in this city, I don't think we've done anyone any favors. Nor have we done our job. Let me ask you this, Dan: What do you hope to accomplish by this story? Is this just a way to make the administration look bad? Or is there another reason you want to run with this?"

"Believe it or not, I'm not trying to make the administration look bad. They can do that by themselves, without any help from me. I do have an agenda here, but it is not one you'd expect." Dan paused. "My sister is a crack addict. The family has pretty much cut her off. But she's still my sister. I see her turning tricks on Third Avenue to pay for her habit. I don't want this guy to get her. Now, don't get me wrong, I don't think that Michelle will stop turning tricks if we run this story. But I do think that there will be more pressure on the administration to devote resources to this investigation. I also think that this story could generate some tips that might help the cops. It is possible that someone has seen something, someone has the clue that the police need to break this case. My interest is personal, but it is public as well. If the public doesn't know there is a problem, they can't help find the killer."

"So you want to use this station to help protect your sister?" asked John Nuggins.

"Not just my sister, John," retorted Dan angrily. "Everyone's sister, daughter, brother, and son. All of those victims have families. And what if this guy decides it is not enough to kill the dealers and the prostitutes? What if he turns to the users and johns? Don't we owe the citizens of this city the information? Yes, I have a personal interest in this story. Are you trying to tell me you've never had a personal interest in a story? Doesn't that interest give you the motivation to get the story?"

"And what about . . . ," Peter interrupted. The others in the room turned to look at him. "There is the possibility that this killer has been at work in other cities. If we run this story, we might get more information, from other cities where this guy has been active. There might also be more help in running the investigation. We have a duty to the public."

"And the public has a duty, too," said Dan. "If they know there is a serial killer out there, they will help. This guy has relatives, maybe a wife, people who know him. They might have noticed things, but not know what he's doing. They might have heard him talking about prostitutes and dealers and how they should be cleaned out of the city. If we publicize this story, people might come forward with the names of possible suspects. Also, it is possible that users and johns have noticed things but didn't realize their importance. They might have the key to catching this guy."

"I hadn't considered that," mused John Nuggins, privately thinking about the prostitute he visited on a regular basis.

"What do you think, Sarah?" asked Mr. Murtock.

"Unfortunately, the legal ground is murky. A year ago, I would have said, no problem, legally we could run the story. But with the Revised Patriot Act, it is not clear. Conceivably, the police could say that this serial killer is no different from a terrorist, and thus we're violating the Patriot Act by publicizing information that the cops don't want out there. There haven't been any cases on this. It is conceivable that Dan and this station could be charged with interfering in an investigation or with obstruction of justice. It depends on the judge and how mad the police get. Having said that, I do think we have to remember our responsibility under the First Amendment. The public does expect us to keep them informed. If nothing else, airing this story will put pressure on the police to do more. The media is part of the checks and balances in our system. In spite of the changes in this country, that still means something. Personally, I would like to challenge this aspect of the Patriot Act in court, but that would be lengthy and costly."

Mr. Murtock shook his head, thinking that things used to be so much easier. Before the national furor over terrorism, these decisions were difficult, but not impossible. The government respected the freedom of the press, and the press, for the most part, acted responsibly. Now every story raised legal questions. Things were so much easier before the changes in the law. While there was something appealing about running stories that would force a legal challenge of the new law, what if he lost?

"Well, Mr. Murtock, are we going to show the stories or not?" asked Peter. Mr. Murtock was looking off into the distance.

"Maybe . . . ," started Dan. The others in the room turned to look at him. "Maybe you should make your decision as if the new law wasn't in existence. What does your gut tell you to do?"

"Algnon!" exclaimed Sarah. The men looked at her quizzically. "I'm sorry, but I just remembered why Sunarke sounded so familiar. He signed a new contract with Algnon last year, didn't he?"

"Yes," said Peter. "That is one of the corporations that is supporting his government, and Algnon is a major campaign contributor to President Crawford. So?"

"I'm sorry, but . . ." Sarah took a deep breath. "Isn't your brother-in-law the CEO of Algnon, Mr. Murtock?"

"Yes, but that is not relevant here," scowled Mr. Murtock. "Really, that is not part of my concern about Peter's story. The man is a pig, and I avoid him whenever possible."

Peter sighed. His Pulitzer was going into the garbage can. Mr. Murtock would not run a story that would hurt his brother-in-law's corporation. Mr. Murtock took a deep breath. "All right, people, this is what we're going to do . . . ."

Points to Ponder

Agree or disagree with the following statements, and give your reasons:

1. Peter was right to just shoot his footage. The media has a duty to report the news, not to influence events.

2. Peter should have warned the Americans in some way. Even though some of the Americans were out of control, not all were. The soldiers did not have a choice in where they were based.

3. The news media in this country has too much power and too much protection from the courts.

4. Is it moral to show our opponents in a favorable light? When Americans are fighting and dying, shouldn't the media be restricted from showing stories that undermine the American position?

5. America has a long history of supporting the dictator against the common people, and this is why so many people hate Americans.

6. It is understandable that sometimes in war soldiers perform acts of inhumanity.

7. All media outlets and reporters have an agenda, just like Peter and Dan have their own agendas. These agendas bias what we learn from the media.

8. The public is not ready for women to be combatants. Even though women want equality and are capable of performing the functions of combatants, it is right that Congress refuses to allow women in these roles.

9. News outlets should be held responsible for the damage done by their stories, by having fines levied against them to compensate those who are injured.

10. Peter should be arrested and tried as a combatant, just as happened with John Walker Lindh. He had information that would have helped U.S. troops and did not use it.

11. Dan is right: his news story needs to be shown. If nothing else, this will protect future victims.

12. Running the story on the serial killer would harm the police investigation. While the public has a right to know, sometimes the best thing is to let the police do their job.

13. Without the threat of the story breaking, most police wouldn't investigate crimes when the victims are not "respectable" people, as in this case.

14. The police in general devote more time and resources to solving the killings of white people than to solving the killings of people of color.

15. Dan's personal interest taints the story. It shouldn't be shown.

Essay Questions

1. The mass media in this country have extraordinary power and protections, particularly in comparison to other countries. Discuss the pros and cons of this situation and any changes you would make to it.

2. There are constant charges of bias in the media today. During the time of the Founders, the media was blatant in its bias and made no claim to be objective. Would it be better to go back to that system, whereby we would know the political persuasion of the ownership of the media outlet? Is it possible to have an unbiased media?

Chapter 11

The People's Talking Shop: Congress

W "ell, David, do we have the votes?" asked White House chief of staff Fred Winkle.

"Yes, Fred," replied White House legislative assistant David Brown. "With our party controlling both houses of Congress there really isn't much doubt. Everything went well in the Conference Committee. We've worked out all of the compromises. This is a bill that both the House and the Senate can support. There will be no more amendments. So the president will get what he wants. The bill passed the House with a comfortable majority. Debate in the Senate started this morning. As soon as all of the senators have weighed in, they'll vote, and the Gun Legislation Reform Act will pass. Gun companies will receive the same protections as tobacco received, and there will be a limit on how many handguns an individual can own. You can tell the president it's a done deal."

⋆ ⋆ ⋆

"Mr. President."

"The chair recognizes the senior senator from Illinois. Mr. Witowski, you have the floor."

"Thank you. I realize that everyone here wants to vote on this bill so they can go home. However, in good conscience I need to speak my mind, not only to reflect what the good people of Illinois think, but also to reflect on what is in the best interest of this country. As you know, my parents came here after World War II as refugees from Poland. They settled in a Polish neighborhood, worked hard, relied on the community for support, and became small-business owners. They did what millions of other immigrant families did. They worked hard, raised their children, and improved their standard of living." Other senators were nodding, having heard the story before. They did not expect anything different today.

"One night, as my parents were getting ready to close their shop for the evening, a group of young men came in to rob them. During the robbery, my father was shot and killed; my mother was wounded but survived. Based on my personal history, the White House, party leadership, interest groups like the NRA and other gun lobbies that have supported me, interest groups that support the Gun Legislation Reform Act, and colleagues on the Hill have all presumed I would support this legislation. They are wrong!" Senator Stan Witowski paused, watching the startled reaction on the floor of the Senate. "Not only do I not support this legislation, I am prepared to stand here talking until the rest of this august body agrees with me."

Many of the senators on the floor visibly blanched. Witowski was going to filibuster. At the White House, David Brown, who had been all but ignoring the television coverage of the debate, fell out of his chair. Picking himself up, he rushed to Fred Winkle's office, turning on the television there. As Fred looked at David incredulously, David blurted out, "We have a problem. The bill might not go through after all. Witowski is going to filibuster." Behind him, the television showed Senator Witowski continuing to speak.

"I have been assured that this legislation is necessary to protect the gun manufacturers in this country. We all know this bill was essentially written by gun lobbyists to protect their interest groups. We also all know that individuals and cities are suing the manufacturers for damages caused by guns. It has even been argued that guns are a faulty product. I listened to these arguments when I was in the House and the tobacco legislation was being debated. I am ashamed to say that at that time I did not have the courage of my convictions and therefore did not oppose that bill. At that time I was more concerned with getting reelected than doing what was in the best interest of the country. I also could not have stopped that bill in the House. This time it is different. I can and will stop this bill here in the Senate. This may mean I will not be reelected. If that is the case, so be it. As a United States senator, I have a responsibility to represent my constituents. However, even though several cities in Illinois have joined in lawsuits against gun companies, I cannot vote for this bill. The people of Illinois sent me here to do what I think best. That is the nature of representative democracy. Some might argue that I am supposed to do what the people of Illinois sent me here to do. That I am supposed to vote only in the interests of the people of Illinois. And the majority of the people in my state do support this bill. However, I disagree. I am supposed to do what I feel is best, not just for the people of Illinois, but for the people of this great country. I am probably ending my political career here today, but I will have my say. I agree that something must be done about the lawsuits threatening the gun industry. But instead of creating a fund and indemnifying the companies, we should take another option. Because, if we are not careful, in a few years we will be debating a bill to save the liquor industry or the automobile manufacturers.

"And I'm not even mentioning the amendments to this bill. I doubt the American public would support this bill if they were aware of the fact that one of the amendments establishes an $80 million fund to study the reasons prisoners want to escape from prison. Another amendment gives funding for low-income daycare. And yet another funds the expansion of several interstate highways. None of these has anything to do with the problems associated with guns but were tacked on so that some congressmen can get support for their pet projects. In other words, this is pork. We need to stop this practice so that only germane amendments would be allowed. If you have a pet project, let it stand or fall on its own merits. But let me get back to the point.

"If this bill had been law when my father was killed, my mother and I would have been entitled to compensation from the gun manufacturers. To take that money would have been an insult to everything my parents believed in and taught me. The gun manufacturers were not responsible for what happened in my parents' store, but according to this bill, the manufacturers would pay compensation. That is wrong.

"Instead, I propose we kill this bill and pass the Personal Responsibility Act. I was raised to believe you are responsible for your own actions, both the good and the bad. When I failed my high school geometry class, my parents did not assume it was because I had a bad teacher or the teacher was prejudiced against Poles or anything else. My parents concluded that I was responsible, that I didn't study hard enough. And they were right. That attitude is missing from our society today. No one is willing to take responsibility for their actions. They want the government to watch over them like children. As far as I'm concerned, that is not the government's job. People must take responsibility for themselves. If we are concerned about the gun industry in this country, the best thing we can do for them is to pass the Personal Responsibility Act, rather than the Gun Legislation Reform Act. The gun industry will not be helped by this legislation; it will only serve as a Band-Aid, disguising the greater problem. You know, my son is in college. He comes home and tells me interesting things. Apparently, some American Indian tribes have something called the Seven Generation rule. Essentially what this means is that before you do anything, you consider the ramifications for the next seven generations. We need to adopt that type of thinking in the Congress. We have too great a tendency to take a short-sighted view of things. We focus on what is necessary to get reelected, rather than what is in the best interest of the long-term development of this country. The Founding Fathers did look at things for the long term; that is why our Constitution is still in effect after more than 200 years. We must begin thinking along those lines."

★   ★   ★

"This is Ann Tyler, for Satellite News Service. I'm speaking from outside the Capitol. Inside, Senator Stan Witowski has begun a filibuster on the

Gun Legislation Reform Act. For those of you who are not up on your civics lessons, Senator Witowski has essentially stopped all business in the Senate while he details his objections to this bill. It is within his power to keep the Senate from acting on this bill entirely. There are steps to force a vote, but cloture, which would force the vote, is very difficult to implement."

"Ann, this is Bill Smithers." Ann looked startled at the interruption. "Yes, Bill?"

"Why do you think Senator Witowski has chosen this time to filibuster? Surely he could have raised his objections to the bill earlier." Bill looked mystified.

"Yes, Bill," replied Ann slowly, "Senator Witowski could have raised his objections earlier. However, that would not have been as effective. The president and members of his party could have then put pressure on him to withdraw his opposition. By staging a filibuster, he forces everyone in the Senate to listen to his objections. This will also force the White House and the public to think about the points he raises. If he feels strongly enough about this bill, as it appears he does, he can tie up the Senate for days on end."

"Well, Ann," mused Bill, "I don't think that's very democratic. As a matter of fact, I think that's downright un-American!"

Ann took a deep breath. "Actually, Bill, what Senator Witowski is doing is very American. He is standing up for what he believes in against overwhelming odds. Why don't we listen to his reasons for opposing the bill?"

★   ★   ★

The television screen showed the Senate chamber, where numerous senators were watching Witowski, who ignored them all, continuing with his speech.

"We here in Congress have passed a multitude of laws and regulations covering everything from how an ashtray must break to how a company must treat its employees. All of these laws and regulations were implemented with the best intentions, but we have gone too far. Government is necessary to protect the peoples' lives, liberty, and property. However, we have become a nation of irresponsible citizens, asking the government to be like Mommy and Daddy. This is too much. If something goes wrong in our lives, we don't look to ourselves anymore, we decide who we can sue.

"Let me describe some of the lawsuits that have been filed in this country in the past year, based on the research of my staff. In New Jersey, a student has sued his high school for not giving him an adequate education that would enable him to get into the college of his choice. In Wisconsin, a woman sued the landlord of her apartment building because when she was carrying a load of laundry down the outside steps in the snow, she fell and broke her ankle. The laundry weighed forty pounds, and she had a blood-alcohol level three times the level for a drunk-driving conviction, but she's arguing the landlord should have put a second banister on the five steps, which were already covered with slip-resistant material. In Arkansas, a thirty-year-old man is suing his parents for not raising him with enough discipline. He argues that this permissive parenting allowed him to become the drug addict that he is today. In Connecticut, a man is suing fast-food franchises because he didn't know that the food was fattening. In numerous states, people are suing their sexual partners for transmitting STDs. In Texas, a man is suing a corporation because the stocks he purchased are going down in value. In Hawaii, a convicted felon is suing the owner of the home he burgled for compensation for the injuries he received while he burglarized the home. I could go on and on with the examples and probably will later. The point here is that none of these people are willing to take responsibility for their own actions."

In the office of the chief of staff, David and Fred looked at one another. While Fred listened to the senator with gloom on his face, David was calling the Senate office buildings, trying to find the majority leader or majority whip, hoping to find some way to blackmail Senator Witowski into stopping the filibuster. Senator Witowski continued talking, aware of the consternation he was causing, but beyond caring.

"If my child is shot in a drive-by shooting, who is responsible? The gun maker? The carmaker? Or the person shooting the gun? As far as I'm concerned, both the gun and the car are doing what they were designed to do. Likewise, my maternal grandmother, a two-pack-a-day smoker, died from emphysema. Was that the fault of the tobacco company? No! She could have quit smoking if she wanted to. I know the arguments that say tobacco companies are putting chemicals into cigarettes to make them more addictive. I am also aware of the fact that this government mandates that tobacco leaves contain certain levels of nicotine, the primary addictive element. Even though growers have the ability to grow less addictive tobacco, they don't, because it does not meet federal standards. The bottom line is that thousands of people quit smoking every year. It is difficult, but they do it. We here in the Senate must take a stand and tell Americans that they are responsible for their own lives. The Personal Responsibility Act could also be called the Common Sense Act. Common sense tells you what to do in each of the examples I've given.

"I propose a federal law mandating that all such proposed lawsuits must first be presented to a panel of three federal judges who will decide whether the case should be allowed to be filed or whether common sense dictates otherwise. This will allow Americans to begin taking responsibility for their actions while protecting companies with deep pockets from nuisance lawsuits. And it would ensure that lawsuits with merit could proceed and hold accountable companies or persons who are acting in ways that endanger our country. Reform is necessary.

"My bill would also regulate attorneys' fees. Too many attorneys work on a contingency basis and therefore have an incentive to file frivolous lawsuits. This must be changed. In several states doctors are going on strike because they can't afford their malpractice premiums. The majority of them are good doctors, but because of contingency fees, attorneys are filing lawsuits against doctors, just to settle out of court. This has led to huge malpractice premiums. This needs to be stopped. In my home state, teachers and policemen are now purchasing malpractice insurance, to protect themselves against lawsuits. People in this country will sue over anything, and lawyers are willing to support them. This needs to be changed. Likewise, we need to regulate the fees attorneys charge in criminal trials. It is essentially wrong that wealthy defendants can buy justice while poor defendants are incarcerated. I see that some of the senators are shaking their heads at my apparent naiveté.

"While I'm saying that there is too much regulation in this country, I'm also asking for regulations on attorneys. That is because they are part of the problem. With contingency fees they have a great incentive to file lawsuits, hoping that the companies or individuals will settle out of court. I am an attorney and have taken money from lobbyists for attorneys. But I feel the situation has gotten out of hand. Instead of serving justice, our attorneys are serving greed. My three-judge panel will not only determine which lawsuits go forward, but how much the attorneys can charge. Limiting attorneys' fees in criminal cases will be easy. I have a schedule of fees for a wide variety of crimes. This would be implemented nationally. It will also speed up the court system—attorneys will no longer have an incentive to drag cases out and rack up more fees. I'll talk more about this later. Now I want you to see why I feel this reform is necessary.

"Now let me be clear: legitimate problems can still be pursued under my bill. When you start talking about nuisance lawsuits almost everyone brings up the McDonald's coffee case." Stan looked around and saw his colleagues nodding. "Let's get some facts on that case. It is true that the eighty-one-year-old woman was awarded punitive damages of $2.7 million. However, on appeal that was reduced to $480,000. Why did the jury award this woman so much money? Was it because she had sharp lawyers? No. If you or I go to the Senate dining room for a cup of coffee, what we will receive will be coffee of a temperature of roughly 155 degrees. And as you know, that still scorches the tongue. McDonald's keeps its coffee at 185 degrees—a temperature that can cause severe burns within two to seven seconds. And prior to this lawsuit, McDonald's had settled more than 700 cases of scalding coffee burns. They knew they had a problem and did nothing about it. That is why the jury decided the way it did." Stan looked around at the shocked faces of the other senators before continuing. "Now, some of you are thinking, "What a hypocrite. He wants Americans to take personal responsibility, but he's ignoring the fact that the woman was driving with the coffee—which is illegal and also why she was burned." And you're right, to an extent. My bill would have only allowed the woman to collect for medical expenses, because she was partially at fault. But the three-judge panel would have allowed the case to go to trial, on the grounds that McDonald's was presenting a danger to the public.

"Think about it this way. I go to McDonald's and get a cup of coffee. While walking to my table to drink it, your six-year-old grandson runs into me, bumping my arm. The coffee spills on him, leaving third-degree burns on his head and neck. McDonald's is responsible for the temperature of their coffee. The Personal Responsibility Act would allow product liability lawsuits if they are valid claims like this one. But it would not allow these nuisance lawsuits, like the cities suing gun makers to cover the costs of drive-by shootings. My fellow senators, we need to make a stand here and now . . ."

★   ★   ★

"Damn that man," exclaimed President Sommers. "Can't they just shut him up? If he keeps talking he will kill this bill."

"That, unfortunately, Mr. President, is the point of the filibuster," observed Fred Winkle. "In the Senate you can talk a bill to death if you have the stamina."

"Is he telling the truth?" asked the president. "Did anyone ask him how he felt about the bill? I know that no one ever suggested I talk to him."

"Unfortunately, Mr. President," replied David weakly, "I never talked to him. The party assured me he would support the bill."

"I want to see the whip in my office. I want him to explain who dropped the ball here, and I want him to put a stop to this," commanded the president. "Does Witowski realize that hundreds of hours of work went into this bill? Does he realize how much time will have been wasted if he kills this bill?"

"I'll see if I can get the whip," muttered David.

Fred glared at David, who slipped out of the Oval Office. "Mr. President, Witowski does realize that. But one of the principles of the Founders was that it should be very difficult to pass a bill. They wouldn't view this as wasted time. The Founders would argue that the time was well spent, as it allowed members of Congress to explore the pros and cons of the issue. The Founders wanted as few laws as possible restricting the liberty of Americans."

"Can't someone just call for a vote?" asked the president, shaking his head at the stupidity of the filibuster.

"No. Senator Witowski has the floor as long as he keeps standing and talking. Just be grateful that he hasn't started reading recipes into the record," replied Fred sourly.

★ ★ ★

"Ann, can you enlighten our viewers for us?" asked Bill Smithers. "Aren't there rules in the Senate limiting how long an individual senator can talk? I know that the House limits the debate on a bill. Why don't they limit debate in the Senate?"

Ann smiled grimly. "Bill, the Founders would have approved of the way the Senate handles debate. They wanted as much debate as possible. The House adopted rules to limit debate because, with 435 members, if there were unlimited debate nothing would ever get done. However, the Senate has consistently refused to limit debate. There are only 100 senators, and few will ever consider a filibuster. Still, senators jealously guard this privilege. They see it as a way of ensuring their independence and preserving democracy. This is a way for individual senators to make their views known to a large percentage of the population. It is also a way for one person to have dramatic effect on the legislation of this country."

"So, what you're saying, Ann," replied Bill, "is this is a way for Witowski to make his name known, possibly as a first step to running for the presidency."

"No, Bill," snapped Ann, exasperated, "that is not what I'm saying. It is highly unlikely Senator Witowski will run for president. He will be lucky to be reelected after this filibuster. The president and other members of the party will punish him for the filibuster by refusing to support any of his programs. However, Witowski feels strongly about this and is willing to use the rules of the Senate to force the country to rethink its support of the issue. Not every politician does things solely to get reelected or run for higher office. Witowski is standing up for his principles, something very few politicians do these days."

"I see," responded Bill. "We're being joined in the station by Representative Joe Smally, Democrat from Tennessee. Congressman, you were one of the main authors of this bill. What do you think of what Senator Witowski is doing?"

"Well, Bill, I agree with you," said the representative slowly. "Senator Witowski is an honorable man; I remember serving with him in the House. But if he were in the House and had authored a bill that was being filibustered in the Senate, he would be furious. *I* am furious. Witowski has a right to his opinion, but he is going against the wishes of his constituents and the majority of citizens. The Senate should get rid of the filibuster."

Ann interrupted the representative. "Tell me, Congressman, you were strongly opposed to the president's antiabortion initiative. Wouldn't you have liked to be able to stop the passage of that bill by using a filibuster? Isn't your objection just based on the fact that this is your bill? If you opposed this bill, wouldn't you be applauding Senator Witowski's actions?"

"Ann," replied the congressman somberly, "we live in a democracy. That means that the will of the people should reign. This is essentially vetoing the will of the people."

Bill jumped back into the discussion. "Ann, we've had Trisha doing 'man in the street' interviews. Why don't you watch with the rest of us, to see what the public thinks of Witowski's filibuster?"

★　★　★

The monitor showed a young blond reporter, joined by an elderly black woman. "My name? Wanda Evers. I don't care about the rules of the Senate. This senator, Witwoska you said his name is? He doesn't know what it is like to live in a war zone. My daughter was killed in a drive-by five years ago, and I'm raising her three kids. One of them is already in a gang, because he was threatened so many times by members of other gangs. There are guns being fired in our neighborhood every night. We've got to put a stop to all the guns on the street."

"My name is Paul Jones. Yes, I'm familiar with the filibuster. While I'm not sure I agree with the Senator's reasons for his filibuster, I do think something needs to be done. I don't think we need to get rid of the filibuster; it does help the country sometimes. But realistically, Witowski is not going to be facing the voters for another five years. I think that we need to change that. I think that any senator who launches a filibuster should face the voters within six months. That way the voters can decide whether or not they agree with the filibuster. Face it, in five years most of the people in Illinois will not remember Witowski's filibuster. If he feels so strongly about this issue, he should be ready to explain his actions to the voters."

"Jesus Gomez. I think we need to get rid of the filibuster. While I understand that the Founders would have loved it, I think it is outdated. Today's government needs to be able to move rapidly; the filibuster is kind of like an appendix—useful once, nothing but a pain today."

"Rita Smith. I think what Senator Witowski is doing is great. I'm a teacher, and I would like to see people taking responsibility for their actions. I don't know if I agree that we shouldn't hold the gun companies responsible, because violence in the schools is a serious problem. But I like the idea of a personal responsibility act."

"Well, Bill, the public doesn't seem to be in support of Senator Witowski's filibuster. I do have to say, though, that many people weren't aware of it. This is Trisha Laud. Back to Bill in the studio."

Points to Ponder

Agree or disagree with the following statements, and give your reasons:

1. Most members of Congress are like Witowski when he was in the House, more concerned about getting reelected than doing what is right.

2. Witowski is too idealistic. Nothing the government can do will force Americans to take responsibility for their actions.

3. The filibuster is a tradition that should be kept, as it allows some courageous senators to force us to stop and reconsider proposed legislation, protecting minority rights.

4. We have too many nuisance lawsuits in this country.

5. An act like the one that Witowski proposes would do more harm than good.

6. Witowski is wrong: gun companies should be held liable for the damage done by their products. It is no different than holding companies liable for damage to the environment.

7. The threat of lawsuits is the only thing keeping some businesses from producing faulty or dangerous products.

8. Attorneys often file frivolous lawsuits hoping companies will settle out of court.

9. It is wrong that one man like Witowski can force Congress to grind to a halt and kill legislation supported by the majority of the citizens.

10. It is too difficult for Congress to pass legislation. The process should be streamlined for the good of the country.

11. The House should adopt a mechanism like the filibuster. It is an important part of the checks and balances.

12. Members of Congress should vote along party lines, even if they disagree with the party stance.

13. Witowski took money from lobbyists supporting this bill. Therefore he should vote for it.

14. Witowski is right—in this country the wealthy can buy justice. The system needs to be reformed.

15. There is too much pork in Congress. We need to educate the public to penalize representatives who insist on wasting money on pork.

16. It is too easy to add amendments to bills. Congress will not reform this practice, so we should have a constitutional amendment banning amendments that are not germane.

17. We should adopt seven-generation thinking, as Witowski advocates. Our country tends to ignore the long-term effects of our policies.

18. Representative Smally is right: the filibuster is a way to thwart the will of the majority. That is wrong in a democracy.

19. The man in the street is right: senators should be subject to an election within six months of a filibuster.

Essay Questions

1. Discuss the problems you see with the legislative branch of our national government. How would you resolve them?

2. Discuss the nature of representation in our system. How should representatives resolve the conflict between what they think is best for the country and what their constituents want? Between the interests of the nation and those of the state or locality that elected the member of Congress?

Chapter 12

Hail to the Chief:
The Presidency

Professor Shannon Jackman frowned. The meeting was not going to be pleasant. Charles had put a lot of work into his dissertation. The members of the committee appreciated that. It was just that the dissertation was a little too radical in some places. Charles would have to have a strong defense if he wanted her signature approving the final document.

Charles took a deep breath. It was unusual for all three committee members to demand a meeting before signing a dissertation. Usually they met with him individually. The only time they would all meet together was during the oral defense. But the committee had told him that he would not even have an opportunity to present an oral defense unless he addressed their concerns. He took another deep breath and entered Professor Jackman's office. There, sitting with grim faces, were the members of his committee: Professor Jackman, Professor Arnold Troy, and Professor Felix Robles. All were specialists in various aspects of the American presidency.

"Good morning, Charles," said Professor Jackman. "Thank you for meeting with us. We know this is unorthodox, but while we've each seen individual parts of your dissertation, it is only now that we have each seen the completed work. It raises some concerns."

"I know that, Professor Jackman," replied Charles.

"It is important that you realize, Charles," said Felix Robles gently, "that this is not an inquisition. This is a meeting of four highly educated, intelligent individuals, wherein we will discuss aspects of the American presidency, *as equals*. Please, drop the 'Professor.' We are all on a first-name basis here."

Charles breathed a sigh of relief. If they were all equals that meant his dissertation would be approved. He nodded.

Arnold Troy gave Felix a dirty look. Unlike the other professors, Arnold did like to stand on ceremony. Charles should treat them with the respect that they deserved. He began the questioning. "Tell me, Charles, are you serious about wanting to change the natural-born requirement for the presidency? Do you really feel we should tamper with the work of the Founding Fathers?"

"Yes, sir, I do," Charles responded nervously. No matter what Felix said, there was no way Charles could address Professor Troy by his first name. "Sir" would do. "Essentially, I think the requirement is outdated. At the Constitutional Convention, the Founders were concerned that someone from Britain could come to the United States, become president, and then work to further British interests instead of American interests. At the time, there was some justification for the stipulation. The Founders did not know how well the separation of powers would work, whether Congress could successfully control a president. Today that is no longer a problem. Today there are other problems.

"First, I have questions about whether place of birth necessarily leads to loyalty. For example, if Communist China had infiltrated America with spies in the 1950s, these spies could have lived as normal Americans. They could have had kids, started small businesses, become typical Americans. But secretly they could have taught their children communist doctrine and love for Communist China. When they grew up, one of their children could run for president. There would be no constitutional problem. But that new president would in fact be loyal to China, not America. The natural-born clause is no protection against something like this."

Arnold snorted. "Don't you think that is a little far-fetched? Anyway, how much damage could such a president do? After all, the bureaucracy, Congress, and the Supreme Court dramatically limit the president's ability to do anything."

"Yes, sir, you're right," Charles explained patiently. "But while it is true that Congress can, through the separation of powers and checks and balances, exert a great deal of control over that president, the natural-born clause does not guarantee a president loyal to the United States. Don't you agree?"

"I suppose so," grunted Arnold.

"I'm more interested in your argument about dual nationality," interjected Felix. "Why don't you explain that to me again?"

"All right," smiled Charles. "I have an old family friend, who we called Uncle Tim. Uncle Tim was my father's army buddy. Uncle Tim was a natural-born American. But his mother was from Venezuela. When Dad and Uncle Tim were serving in the Army during Vietnam, Uncle Tim got a draft notice from the Venezuelan army. Because his mother was Venezuelan, according to the Venezuelan government, Uncle Tim was also a Venezuelan citizen. There are more and more people of dual citizenship in the country today. Like Senator Lieberman. As a Jew, Senator Lieberman is entitled to citizenship in Israel. True, he would have to actually apply, but in other cases, like Uncle Tim's, the dual citizenship is automatic. It doesn't matter if the United States recognizes dual citizenship or not. The fact is, some countries give automatic citizenship to the children of citizens, no matter where they are born. In some cases, like Uncle Tim's, the children do not even know about their dual citizenship for much of their lives. In other cases, they may know and prefer to promote the interests of their other country, not those of the United States. Should people with dual citizenship be able to be president of the United States? They fulfill the natural-born citizenship requirement. But that doesn't mean that their primary loyalty is to the United States. Honestly, I was surprised that no one had raised the issue when Lieberman was nominated for the vice presidency in 2000. It was probably because people were afraid of being called anti-Semitic. But the bottom line is there are valid constitutional questions here.

"There are also questions about whether or not that clause is in direct conflict with the Fourteenth Amendment's equal protection clause. The natural-born stipulation is clearly discriminatory against immigrants. If the Fourteenth Amendment covers naturalized citizens, which the Supreme Court obviously feels is the case, then they are being discriminated against by the natural-born clause. Of course, until a naturalized citizen tries to become president and is denied, the Supreme Court is not going to step in. But this country is being denied the possible leadership of some highly intelligent, otherwise qualified people by excluding naturalized citizens from the presidency. Henry Kissinger is an extremely capable man who could never become president, simply by accident of birth. This seems to go against the very founding principles of this country."

"Well," sighed Felix, "that is certainly a novel argument. I'm not sure I agree with you."

"Felix," responded Charles tentatively. It felt strange calling the professor by his first name. "Think about our beliefs and culture. The founders rejected the notion that birth should determine your fate—unless of course you were born a slave. But a major reason for the American Revolution and subsequent Constitution was a rejection of the British principle that your birth determined your place in society. The whole idea was un-American. This is a country established on the belief that your circumstances of birth are irrelevant. What is relevant is what you do with your life. It is just fundamentally wrong to deny a person the chance to become president simply because of the place they were born. We generally don't like to punish someone for something over which they have no control."

Felix nodded. "That actually is a fairly strong argument. I can see that opening up a great deal of discussion about the natural-born clause."

"But there is still a problem," interrupted Arnold. "How do you ensure that the person elected as president is loyal, a patriotic American, if they are not a natural-born citizen? I grant you, birth alone does not guarantee loyalty, but what guarantee do we have that a naturalized citizen will be loyal?"

Charles looked at the professor, silently wishing there were a way to get him replaced on the committee. They would never agree. He took a deep breath and replied, "Well, sir, that is why I'm advocating that a naturalized citizen must have held citizenship for at least 35 years, currently the minimum age for president. If you've been a citizen for 35 years, I think we can be pretty sure you're loyal. I'm also recommending a minimum of 14 years' residency as an adult for anyone who wants to become president, naturalized or natural-born. According to the Constitution, right now someone 35 years old, who was born in this country and lived here until age 15 but then spent the rest of their life in a foreign country, could run for president. They would know very little about our country, but they would meet the constitutional requirements. I think that needs to be changed."

"So do I," Shannon jumped in. "If that were the sole focus of your dissertation, I would sign off with little trouble. But the rest of your arguments bother me. You're advocating fundamentally changing the nature of the American presidency." Arnold nodded his head in agreement with the criticism.

"I realize that," said Charles shakily. "But I do think we need to discuss situations that the founders could never have envisioned. For example, in their time, 35 was middle-aged, 50 was elderly. Things are different today. After all, who wants a 35-year-old president? And, really, as much as I liked Reagan, the man's Alzheimer's had definitely kicked in before he left office. So we need age limits. I don't know where we should draw the line, but we definitely need to do something. I think the minimum age should be at least 40, possibly 45. Maybe we should put the maximum age at 65 or 70."

"Isn't that age discrimination, young man?" asked Arnold nastily.

"Isn't there already age discrimination in the Constitution, sir?" responded Charles. "After all, I'm 30 years old. If I wanted to be president, I can't; I'm considered too young. I think if we have an age minimum, we can have an age maximum. And if it is part of a constitutional amendment, then it is not illegal."

"Really, Arnold, I don't want to get sidetracked here," interrupted Shannon. "That was not what concerned me about this dissertation. But I do have to say that I think Charles is underestimating the intelligence of the American people. They may not understand the intricacies of the Electoral College or the separation of powers, but they do know what feels right. I doubt they would elect someone president who had dual nationality or whose parents were refugees from Communist China."

Before she could go any further, Charles jumped in, hoping to distract her from a point he knew she was going to make. "I realize that in other ways I'm talking about a dramatic change in the office of the presidency, but don't you think we need to explore the idea? I think this country needs to have a discussion of the possibility of breaking the office into two positions. Most countries have a head of state and a head of government. The head of state does all the ceremonial things like christening ships or throwing out the first baseball of the season, while the head of the government runs the country. Given all we ask of the president, that might be a good idea for this country. I realize presidents wouldn't go for that change. Those ceremonial occasions present good photo opportunities that help in reelection. It might be better to adopt the French system. The French president is responsible for foreign affairs, and the prime minister is responsible for domestic affairs. That might be a good system for the United States. After all, most presidents we've had were strong in one area but weak in the other. This would ensure that the country has competent people dealing with our internal problems and foreign affairs. It might be a good idea to make the president responsible for foreign affairs and the vice president responsible for domestic affairs. Realistically, the vice president doesn't have much to do, unless the president asks him to take on a specific job. With each responsible for one aspect of governing, you won't have a president paralyzed by foreign affairs, like Carter was with the Iran hostage crisis. With my system, the vice president would be able to continue to see to the domestic affairs of the country, while the president deals with the foreign affairs."

"That idea has some limited merit, Charles," interrupted Felix, "but what you're ignoring is the fact that it doesn't work well all of the time in France. It has led some governments to fall."

"That's because France has made it a habit to choose their president and prime minister from different parties. That wouldn't be the case here," responded Charles rapidly. At least this was a point he had considered. "We would still elect the president and the vice president from the same party, so they would work together. This would also help in situations where the lines are blurry, like when domestic factories are producing acid rain that affects other countries. Both the president and the vice president would be able to address this problem." Felix nodded, considering the argument.

Arnold shook his head. The problem with students was the fact that they all felt they knew better. There was no reason to change what had been working well for more than two hundred years.

"And what is your justification for eliminating the presidential pardon?" he asked snidely. "I would think you would support it. After all, if you liked Reagan, you're probably glad that Ford pardoned Nixon."

"Actually, no, I'm not. And I'm not advocating eliminating the pardon," Charles said, frustrated. You would think highly educated professors could understand simple English. "If you look at that section of my dissertation, I'm advocating *modifying* the pardon. The president would still have the right to pardon people, but only *after* a conviction. The president would not be able to issue blanket pardons, pardoning someone for any actions that may have been illegal. I have a problem with Ford's pardon of Nixon for that reason. Nixon was not tried. It's theoretically possible that, after the pardon, it could have come out that Nixon routinely assassinated people in the Oval Office, and nothing could have been done about it. The pardon put him above the law. It is my belief that no one in this country should be above the law. The president should only be able to pardon people after they've been convicted. In Nixon's case, I think it would have been best for this country to have tried him for the crimes associated with Watergate. If he had been convicted, then the president could have pardoned him. The president must be subject to the law like everyone else. Since that time there have been numerous other blanket pardons, granted before conviction. I just don't think that is in the best interest of the country. Essentially, if you have enough money to donate to the president, or you have friends in the right place, you can get away with murder."

Arnold frowned. "The vast majority of pardons are after conviction. Let's play 'what if?' What if I were in the right place at the right time and had a gun. I see Osama bin Laden walking down Main Street, USA. I kill him, blow him away. You want to try me for murder and then hope the president gives me a pardon? Sometimes it is in the nation's best interest to put some actions or people above the law."

"Okay, sir, let's continue with your 'what if?'" responded Charles confidently. "What if you did kill that man walking down Main Street? And it turns out it wasn't Osama, just his look-alike? We have laws for a reason. By your logic, I should be able to kill the guy who was talking about raping my five-year-old sister and then ask the president for a pardon. All I'm asking is that people be held responsible for their actions. If you did kill bin Laden, and I was on the jury, I don't know if I would vote to convict. But if you were convicted, then I'm sure you would get the fastest pardon in history. What I'm saying is that the way it works today, we don't have equality before the law. The president would still be able to pardon, under my system, but first the legal system in this country would do its job. Otherwise, we run the risk of vigilantes. As it is, we've got people who break the law, believing that their friends will get them out of trouble. I don't think that is in the best interest of the country."

"And you think a trial of Nixon would have been in the best interest of the country? Watergate tore this country apart. The presidency was harmed irrevocably. Wouldn't a trial have destroyed this country?" asked Arnold.

"I have faith in this country," replied Charles. "The pardon damaged the country and the presidency. I don't think a trial would have done worse."

Shannon jumped in again. She was not going to be deterred from pursuing her point. "All of this about the pardon is interesting, but Charles, do you think a woman can be president? Or are you just another misogynist who can't stand the thought of a woman in a position of power? Realize this: Women are not going back to the kitchen. They are in politics, and one day a woman will win the presidency. I really can't understand why you would even consider arguing that a woman can't be president. Women are just as capable as men, some even more so. I could argue that the country would be better off if women had won some of the recent elections. As far as your precious Reagan goes, we might not have as many problems in this country if it had been Nancy elected instead of Ronald." Felix and Arnold groaned. Shannon was going feminist on them again.

"Really, Shannon, this is precisely why no woman will ever be president," joked Arnold. "When you go off on your PMS rants, you just show why a woman shouldn't hold that office. I mean, really, one hormone surge and the nukes are suddenly flying."

"Well, Arnold, we've just seen why you won't be president!" snapped Shannon. "Fortunately, most people don't hold the same view of women as you do. And for your information, a woman can get angry without being influenced by hormones. I'm sure Nixon would have liked to be able to say Watergate was just something that he didn't realize he was doing because of menopause; no one made that argument. Believe it or not, women are not driven by their hormones—unlike Clinton. Just look at Maggie Thatcher or Golda Meir. They were perfectly capable of running their countries. Unfortunately, there are too many men like you in this country, men who don't realize that women are capable."

Charles gulped. Arnold had just made the situation much worse than he feared. Charles had hoped to avoid this discussion. That was why all of the drafts of this section of the dissertation had gone only to Felix. Felix nodded at Charles, encouraging him to defend his point of view. Charles started gingerly, but his voice became stronger as he developed his argument. "I realize this part of the dissertation makes me look more conservative than Patrick Buchanan or even Hitler, but if you listen, you will see I'm not saying women shouldn't be president, I'm saying that I don't know if the Constitution *allows* them to become president."

Shannon Jackman glared at Charles and flicked her hand, motioning him to continue.

"Essentially, it is my belief that if we are adhering to the strict language of the Constitution, it's not clear if a woman is entitled to become president. The Constitution never specifically says that only men can run for office. The Constitution itself refers to 'citizens' or 'people,' not to 'men.' Voter qualifications, one indicator of how the founders felt about this issue, were left to the states. However, all personal pronouns in the Constitution itself are masculine: 'he,' 'his,' and 'him.'" Charles avoided looking at Shannon, directing his argument to Felix and Arnold, who were nodding in agreement. "Therefore, if the language of the Constitution is the deciding factor, as it is with the natural-born-citizen clause, then it seems to me that the Founders explicitly prohibited women from running for any federal office. Otherwise the Founders would have used different pronouns. The fact is, the Supreme Court has often ruled that the Founders chose their words carefully, and those words were important.

"For example, the Bill of Rights starts out 'Congress shall make no law . . .' The Supreme Court ruled that this wording meant that the Bill of Rights applied only to the federal government, not to the state governments. It took a long time and many cases before the Court applied the Bill of Rights to the state governments. It still has not applied the entire Bill of Rights to the states. Therefore exact words are important, and thus the fact that the Founders used masculine pronouns is important.

"And the Fourteenth Amendment specifically gave the right to vote to male citizens, rejecting that right for women. By implication, it could be argued that this insertion of the word 'male' in the Fourteenth Amendment meant that all other rights were available to both male and female, but that would be a difficult argument to make.

"The Nineteenth Amendment does not solve the problem. That amendment solely addresses voting rights. It could be interpreted to apply retroactively to qualifications for holding public office, but I haven't been able to find any Court decisions supporting that point of view. And then there is the Supreme Court's decision in *Minor v. Happersett*. In 1875, the Court rejected the argument that citizenship automatically conferred voting rights to women. By extension, citizenship does not automatically confer the right to run for office. You must be a citizen before you can be considered for voting rights. And just because you have the right to vote doesn't mean you automatically have the right to run for office. Given the fact that the language used by the Founders for presidential qualifications was more restrictive than that for any other office, a strong argument can be made that the Constitution excludes women from the presidency."

"What about Geraldine Ferraro's candidacy?" interrupted Shannon. Didn't that show a woman could be president? After all, the party accepted her, states allowed her name to appear on the ballot, and many people voted for her."

"Well, you could make that argument," responded Charles. "But I don't think it is enough. It is conceivable that if Mondale and Ferraro had won the election instead of Reagan, someone could have filed suit to prevent Ferraro from taking office because she did not meet the minimum qualifications as set out by the Constitution."

"I don't know, Charles," Shannon sighed. "It seems to me that you're reaching there. It also seems to me that the fact that we have women in Congress, the cabinet, and on the Supreme Court negates your argument."

"No, not quite," said Charles slowly. "This would not apply to other federal officeholders, because the Constitution does not use such exclusive language in detailing the qualifications for those offices. Yes, all the pronouns are male, but the inclusion of the natural-born clause for the president meant the Founders wanted to place additional limitations on who could be president. Therefore, by implication, there are fewer restrictions on who can hold other offices, and so women are free to hold those offices."

"I'm sorry, Charles," said Shannon slowly, "this is just too radical. We have to think about the reputation of the college. While the earlier points you made have some validity, all of these points together make for an extremely radical dissertation. Maybe you should consider revising it, toning it down, so that it isn't so extreme."

"I know you have genuine concerns, I know you all do," replied Charles carefully. "But, in my heart, I believe that these are valid questions that the country needs to address. But is this the best time to address them? Two of the strongest potential candidates for the upcoming presidential election qualify for dual citizenship. This issue needs to be addressed before the primary season begins. Otherwise we might have a constitutional crisis. I'm not trying to say I know better than all of the scholars who have preceded me. I am saying that as an American citizen, I have concerns, valid concerns, about these issues." He looked at the professors, who were listening to him thoughtfully. "And I think if you're honest with yourselves, you'll realize that these issues need to be discussed before we elect our next president. You're right, this is a radical dissertation. But it is possible that this college could get a reputation for being cutting edge, not extremist, for raising important constitutional issues before the election. The matter lies in your hands."

Points to Ponder

Agree or disagree with the following statements, and give your reasons:

1. People of dual nationality should not be allowed to run for president.

2. Naturalized citizens are often more knowledgeable about this country and more patriotic than natural-born Americans. They should be allowed to run for president.

3. We should amend the Constitution, raising the minimum age and instituting a maximum age for the president.

4. Our political culture still says the circumstances of birth are irrelevant, that it is what you do with your life that counts.

5. We do ask too much of the president—the office should be separated into two positions.

6. As the Constitution does not specify male persons or male citizens, women were and are able to enjoy all privileges conferred by the Constitution, including being president.

7. The strict wording of the Constitution should be the determining factor in any question.

8. Charles is trying to make a mountain out of a molehill. The Constitution is vague and open to reinterpretation. It does not need to be amended to address these issues.

9. Charles is underestimating the intelligence of the American people. They are not likely to elect someone president who left this country at age fifteen or who has dual nationality.

10. Charles is right: the presidential pardon needs to be modified so that it can only be given after a person is convicted of a crime.

11. There have been thousands of presidential pardons. Only a few were blanket pardons or pardons before conviction. There is no reason to alter the Constitution; let presidents continue with an unrestricted right to pardon.

12. Regardless of Charles's argument, the country is not ready for a woman as president, as shown by Arnold's attitude.

13. Having a maximum age for president is a bad idea. One of the reasons the Constitution has lasted so long is the fact that it is vague. It is conceivable that medical science will make advances, and in a hundred years seventy will be considered middle-aged.

14. Arnold is right: the bureaucracy, judiciary, Congress, and the media are strong enough checks on the president that we don't need to worry about the possibility that the president's primary loyalty is not to the United States.

15. Charles is right: we should raise the minimum age for president. There is no way that a thirty-five-year-old is experienced enough to run this country.

16. Charles is focusing on the wrong things: we should amend the constitutional requirements for the job of president to include college graduation, a knowledge of foreign affairs certified by examination, and an understanding of the fundamentals of the Constitution, demonstrated

by passing a test like the one immigrants take to become naturalized citizens.

Essay Questions

1. Discuss the position of president of the United States. Did the Founders expect too much of one person? Have we evolved to the point where we should formally allocate some of those duties to the vice president?

2. Discuss the constitutional requirements for the position of president. Are they too restrictive? Should they be changed? In what ways?

Chapter 13

Cutting Red Tape:
The Bureaucracy

Sheldon, the president would like to see you. Now. I explained to the chief of staff that you had appointments all morning, but he wants to see you right away." Joan looked at her boss helplessly. "I'll work on rescheduling your morning appointments."

"Damn," said Sheldon Whiley, "I don't have time for this today. Do you have any idea of what this is about?" Joan mutely shook her head. "All right, I'll be back when you see me."

"Give me a minute, Mr. Whiley," said the personal assistant to the president. "He's expecting you, but he's not quite finished with the secretary of defense."

Sheldon nodded his head and sat down to wait. He wondered why the president wanted to see him. There was nothing urgent on the agenda. After a few minutes, he was shown into the Oval Office. "Good morning, Mr. President," said Sheldon respectfully.

"No, it most definitely is not a good morning, Sheldon," snapped President Bernie Abrams. "I've got trouble here, and much of it is your fault. What in the hell are you guys doing over there in the Special Office of Bureaucratic Reform? I gave you that job because you seemed like the right man to clean up the federal bureaucracy, starting with the terrible mess we've made of Indian affairs in this country. What is going on? Why haven't you been able to come up with any solutions for me?"

Sheldon sighed. Here we go again, he thought to himself. "Mr. President, as I told you last month, this is not something that can be cleared up easily. Many of the trust accounts for individual Indians and tribes were set up over a hundred years ago. Over time things get lost. I am trying to find the information. After all, some of my own people are party to this lawsuit. I *want* to find out what has happened. But I'm up against bureaucratic inertia—in some cases actual lost information, in other cases hostility from the clerks responsible—and there is an element of outright prejudice within the bureau. Some of the people who work there do not want to help out. In addition, the original instructions from Congress were so broad as to be meaningless. Then there's the problem of federalism and the legacy of the Dawes Act."

"Well, Sheldon, maybe you just need to learn to kick some butt. If the clerks don't want to do their jobs, fire them. I campaigned on the promise to clean up the bureaucracy, using the Bureau of Indian Affairs as an example of the problem. It is up to you to clean up this situation. I realize that things cannot change overnight, but you have got to start. If you fire a few of the worst recalcitrants, the others will fall into line."

Sheldon shook his head wearily. "Mr. President, that is just not feasible. I would love to fire quite a few people. There are still some people working at the BIA who were involved in the sterilization mess of the 1970s. But you can't just fire a civil servant. I and other high-ranking officials serve at the pleasure of the president. If you ask for our resignations, we must give them. However, 95 percent of government workers in this country have civil service protection. In the case of gross misconduct, they can be fired, but only after clear documentation and a series of hearings. It usually takes at least two years to fire someone." Sheldon stopped, seeing that he had finally gotten the attention of the president.

"That's ridiculous. Why are there so many protections? We have some incompetent people. Why can't we just fire them?" President Abrams was aghast.

Sheldon smiled as he replied, "It starts with the Pendleton Act, passed in 1883 after a man who wanted a job in the civil service did not get one and assassinated President Garfield. That started the shift to filling Civil Service positions by competitive exams, rather than patronage. . . . "

"Yes, Sheldon, I went to college, and I'm familiar with the Pendleton Act," Abrams said. "But that doesn't answer my question. I'm not looking for a history lesson here. Just tell me why there are so many protections for civil servants."

"Sir, the Pendleton Act has been broadened and strengthened over time. Most civil servants are prohibited by law from joining unions and have some limits on their First Amendment rights. In return for these restrictions, Congress has given them greater job protection. This way you can't fire someone because they don't support your political program, for example. Many of the civil servants in office today do not support our conservative platform. But if we could just fire them, that would bring this country to a halt. Therefore, when we want to fire someone, there must be clear evidence of incompetence or wrongdoing, and we must show that the person has been given a chance to defend themselves against the accusation. We also must show that the person received notice, was given a chance to improve, things like that. It's so difficult to fire someone that much of the time what happens is they are offered a promotion and transfer to another part of the bureaucracy. They then become someone else's problem."

The president was looking at Sheldon with amusement tinged with anger. "This is ridiculous. If I had run my business like that, I would have been bankrupt in a year."

"Yes, sir, but this is the government, not a business," replied Sheldon seriously. "I know that it sounds absurd, but there is some logic to the system, and there are some benefits. For example, a new president cannot simply come into office and decide to fire everyone associated with the Bureau of Indian Affairs because he thinks the Indians have gotten too much from the federal government. Even if the country supported his views and Congress did too, those employees would have to be absorbed into other bureaucracies. This gives the government bureaucracy some stability. It also means that, for the most part, the people in the bureaucracy know what they are doing. It would not be good for the country to keep getting new people in these positions."

"Well, Sheldon, that just isn't acceptable. I want you to have some of your people start working on a bill to present to Congress. We'll give the bureaucrats a union. That will give them protections against arbitrary action but will allow us to fire people who won't do their jobs or won't cooperate. That will get rid of the Pendleton Act."

"Mr. President, I'm sorry, but it is not that easy. One of the principal strengths of a union is the power to strike. If working conditions get too bad, the members go out on strike. Can you imagine what this country would be like if the bureaucracy went out on strike?" Sheldon shook his head.

The president looked at Sheldon scornfully. "Sheldon, I'm not an idiot. They would not be allowed to strike. Many cities allow their police and firefighters to form unions. The unions are specifically forbidden by law to strike. However, you have union protections of employees. If you've got a cop who consistently comes to work late, you can fire him. The union won't stand in the way because the cop obviously has been derelict in his duty. But if you're just trying to fire this cop because you don't like him, or because he opposes something you're trying to do, the union will prevent the firing. We could do the same thing with the federal bureaucracy. And realistically, the union will help get rid of the deadwood, those people who don't want to do their jobs, those that you can't fire right now. Of course, most likely, those are the people who will become union officers, but since they won't be government workers anymore, it's a way to solve the problem."

"Yes, sir, I'll have my assistant get to work on it right away," replied Sheldon, resigned to the fact that the president had given an order.

"What is the bureaucratic inertia problem you were talking about?" asked the president guardedly, afraid of what the response would be.

"Mr. President, you run into that every day when you ask for information and are told it isn't available, or when you want to change a program and are told it can't be done. Bureaucratic inertia is tied to the fact that the majority of civil servants cannot be fired. Depending on your point of view, it is either a positive aspect of the system or a glaring fault. Essentially, bureaucrats have two powerful attributes. One is the fact that it is almost impossible to fire them, as we've discussed. The other is the fact that they control the information and implement the directives. From your point of view, this is a problem. We need information on those Indian trust accounts. If the bureaucrats disagree with what you, or in this case the judiciary, wants to do with that information, they can drag their feet, making it impossible to get answers. Or imagine that a president wanted to have the information so that he could dissolve the reservations and stop giving Indians preferential treatment. The bureaucrats might not come up with the information necessary. After a lot of foot-dragging, the president might just issue an executive order, directing the bureaucracy to dissolve the tribes. Well, bureaucratic inertia means that the bureaucracy would take forever to do this, until a new president was elected, and the bureaucrats would hope by then the new president would change his mind on this new policy or forget about it.

"Here's another example that might make more sense to you. Do you remember when President George W. Bush appointed that Christian fundamentalist who said, among other things, that women should pray to stop PMS?" The president nodded. "Well, bureaucratic inertia meant that his policies were not implemented. So bureaucratic inertia can be a good thing as well as a bad thing, depending on your point of view. And your union won't take care of inertia. Essentially you would have to prove that the bureaucrats were lying about not being able to find the information. That is next to impossible, particularly with the confused state of our records."

Bernie Abrams was frustrated. "Okay, so what you're telling me is I have to tell members of Congress who are pressuring me on this issue that I can't get the information out of the bureaucrats. This is not going to go over very well. I'm going to look like an incompetent idiot."

"No, sir, you won't," replied Sheldon. "Congress has to deal with the bureaucracy all the time. They know how this works. What you need to keep in mind is the fact that the majority of bureaucrats are good, highly qualified people doing their jobs. A few can really make problems. And in this case, there are some legitimate problems with finding the proper documentation. Think about it this way. Your family has been in this country for over a hundred years. If for some reason a judge ordered you to find the paperwork showing that the first member of your family paid a debt to someone a hundred years ago, would you be able to find the record easily? I doubt it. That is our situation here, but multiplied a hundredfold. Records are hard to find. This is not an excuse, but an explanation."

The president looked at Sheldon. "I am president of the United States. Theoretically I am the most powerful man on earth. You're telling me that some pipsqueak bureaucrat can keep me from doing my job. There is something seriously wrong with this country. That is why I need you to clean up the bureaucracy. Wait a minute. What was that about the sterilizations? You said some people from that time were still working in the BIA. What sterilizations?"

"Mr. President, you are a fundamentally good man, but like many Americans you haven't been educated about some of the things our government has done to American Indians. In the 1970s some doctors working for the Department of the Interior at Indian hospitals decided that Indian women were not good mothers. They were not good mothers because they were poor. These doctors thought the best thing to do would be to sterilize these women. At the very least, several thousand Indian women were sterilized. Most of them were told they would lose their federal benefits if they did not have the operation. Many of them were not properly informed about the fact that the operation would sterilize them; others were told that the operation could be reversed. This policy was supported by segments of the bureaucracy in the BIA. These bureaucrats agreed that Indians should stop having children because they did not know how to raise their children, they were backward, not Christian, or just too poor and ignorant to be parents.

"We still have some of those same bureaucrats working in the BIA today. So when we're looking for billions of dollars owed to Indians, either individuals or tribes, these bureaucrats from the seventies are doing their best to prevent us from finding that money. If the Indians are so incompetent and ignorant, according to this point of view, it would be wrong to give them this money. The Indians would just waste it on alcohol or other frivolous things."

"That is appalling. It sounds like Nazi Germany. Our government forcibly sterilized Indian women?" the president asked.

"Yes, and for almost a hundred years our government forced Indian families to send their children to Christian missionary schools, where they were not allowed to speak their language, practice their culture, or contact their families. But, what is even worse, in some places state welfare departments are telling women, not just Indian women, that they must be sterilized if they want to continue to receive welfare. This is nothing new in this country." Sheldon could not believe a man as educated as the president was unaware of these things. "And then there is the question of Indian remains. . . . "

"Wait a minute, why didn't Congress do something?" asked the president. "Congress holds hearings about everything. Why didn't they hold hearings about the sterilizations?"

"Well, sir, some of the women did write to Congress. One congressman asked the Government Accountability Office to look into it. They did, but only at about half the hospitals. They reported back to the congressman that the problems had been identified and the practice stopped." Sheldon rolled his eyes. "The congressman was satisfied, and nothing else was done."

"Well, why not?" asked the president. "Congress jumps on anything it can. Why didn't the members exploit this for all the political capital they could get?"

"Because, Mr. President, Indians constitute less than 1 percent of our population, and that is not going to get the members of Congress a lot of support at home. This practice was exposed after the Indian Rights Movement, after the occupation of Alcatraz and Wounded Knee. Not too many people were feeling sympathetic to the Indians. The media didn't pay much attention, either. As you know, unless there is media coverage, the public doesn't care." Sheldon shrugged.

"What were you referring to when you mentioned Indian remains?" asked the president.

"Well, sir, at various times in our history, scientists have appropriated Indian remains for research. Many Indian remains are in the Smithsonian. The Indians want them back, so they can be buried," replied Sheldon slowly.

"That makes sense. Who would object to that in this day and age?" asked the president.

"There are some scientists who argue it is important to study these remains, that this will help us learn more about early life in North America. They have filed suit in federal court to prevent the return of the remains to the tribes."

"I suppose there is some justification there," replied the president.

"Mr. President, with all due respect, I have to disagree. How would you like it if your great-grandfather's grave was disturbed? If scientists were able to spend years studying his remains to find out what life was like when he lived? Would you be comfortable with that?"

"No, I don't think so," replied the president slowly. Then he added, "Sheldon, I know you're an old friend, but at least treat the office with respect."

Sheldon was contrite. "I'm sorry, Mr. President. But one of my ancestors has been lying in the Smithsonian for more than fifty years. I would like her put back in the ground where she belongs. I would also like to have the artifacts back."

"I know I'll regret this, but what artifacts?" asked the president.

"Mr. President, the Smithsonian and other branches of the government are holding ceremonial masks, headdresses, capes, and other artifacts belonging to the Indian tribes. Once again, they're saying that these need to be held either for study or to preserve them, that the Indians can't take care of them. From our perspective, these scientists are doing the same thing Hitler wanted to do when he proposed a museum of Jewish history. Our sacred artifacts are on display for anyone to look at, our forebearers are being studied, and our population was almost exterminated as a result of government policy. Like the Jews who were persecuted by

Hitler, we feel entitled to apologies and compensation. We're still waiting for our claims to be acknowledged."

"I was right; I do regret asking that question. Explain to me again about the role of Congress in all this. It's not making sense." The president was looking confused again and definitely wanted to shift this topic.

"Well, sir, the original instructions from Congress were to set up trust funds for the Indians until they were educated enough to become competent to handle their own affairs. Some people argue that the Indians still have not reached that level; if they had, there would no longer be a need for the BIA. The reservations would no longer be federal land, and the Indians would be absorbed into mainstream society. With the new interest in the trust funds, some people in the Bureau feel that Congress is unrealistic, that it is impossible to track down funds from over a hundred years ago. That is the problem with Iron Triangles." Sheldon could see that the president was more confused.

"Let me give you a different example. Congress decides that there are too many teenagers getting pregnant. They pass a law ordering the Department of Health and Human Services to institute programs to reduce the number of teen pregnancies. But that is all Congress says. It is up to HHS to decide if that means more education on birth control, programs on abstinence, free condoms, or more funding for abortions. It is up to the department to implement the order as they see fit. Now, in the BIA, in addition to handling the trust funds for the Indians, we have been instructed by Congress to run the reservations, educate the Indians, teach them trades, help them become 'true Americans.' This is a very broad mandate. Some commissioners for the BIA have used taxpayer money to do this, others have used trust fund money to do it. In some cases the BIA has charged the trust funds for managing the money, in other cases the trust funds have been invested poorly. It is difficult to gather all the necessary information."

"Okay, I'm waiting. Explain 'Iron Triangles' to me," sighed the president.

Sheldon took a deep breath. "All right, sir. A triangle has three points and three sides. Congress is one point, the bureaucracy another, and interest groups the third. In a triangle each side supports the points. So the interest groups support Congress and the bureaucracy, the bureaucracy supports interest groups and Congress, and Congress supports both the bureaucracy and interest groups."

Sheldon paused as the president nodded his head in understanding. "Take the case of Indian sterilization. Interest groups like missionaries and social reform conservatives would have pressured the bureaucracy to perform the sterilizations. They also would have lobbied Congress, saying that this would help the Indians by reducing poverty on the reservations. Congress responds to the interest groups by telling the bureaucracy to reduce poverty on the reservations. The bureaucracy sees this as a way to increase their budget and ensure job security. Everyone is working in their own best interest, so the policy is adopted and difficult to stop. It's difficult to bend or break iron."

"The problem with your explanation, Sheldon," said the president, "is that the Indians can form an interest group to lobby government to stop this practice."

"Yes, sir, but which would have the stronger interest group, social reformers or Indians?" shot back Sheldon.

"What were you saying about federalism being a problem? And the Dawes Act? What's going on there?" asked the president wearily.

"Well, sir, in some cases, particularly in the West, tribes are not recognized by the federal government. The original treaties were signed with state governments, so the tribes do not have federal protections. This means that in some cases the state governments are denying Indians their rights, and in other cases the BIA says it has no jurisdiction. As for the Dawes Act, it dissolved many tribes. Not all tribes were reconstituted in the 1930s, so we have Indians who the government does not recognize as Indians, simply because their tribe no longer exists."

"But there are so many reservations!" exclaimed the president. "Why can't the Indians in tribes that didn't reconstitute just join with other tribes?"

"It is not that easy, Mr. President. Each tribe only has so much money, land, and resources. They can barely take care of themselves in many instances. They can't help thousands of people claiming tribal descent." Sheldon shook his head again.

"What do you mean, 'claiming tribal descent'? Either you're an Indian or you're not." The president was getting exasperated.

"Not according to the government, sir," snapped Sheldon. "For example, take my cousin. He has one-sixteenth Indian blood. The government still considers him an Indian. But if he marries a woman with no Indian blood, their children will not be considered Indians by the government. Just like the Nazis, our government assesses your background to ensure that you have enough Indian ancestors to qualify for benefits."

"We should stop comparing ourselves to Nazis and try to solve these problems fairly. What if we just left it to the tribes to decide who was an Indian? After all, with Indian gaming they now have the resources to help their own people. Combined with the trust fund money they'll be getting, the problems should disappear," the president said, shaking his head. Some people just tried to make things too difficult.

"Sir, I know you're getting frustrated with my repeating this, but it is not that easy." Sheldon took a deep breath. "First of all, many of the tribes have historic enemies. Telling tribes to take in other Indians is like telling the U.S. government to give citizenship to huge numbers of Mexicans because they used to live in this land. Indian gaming has helped some tribes, but most are not benefiting from it at all. And it is dividing the Indians. Those without gaming want money from those who have gaming. And those tribes that have gaming are finding all kinds of people coming out of the woodwork, claiming Indian blood and a right to share in the profits. Greed has created numerous problems. And, finally, without sovereignty, the money doesn't make much difference."

"Now the Indians want sovereignty? Sheldon, I'm sympathetic to their plight, but that is going too far." The president began pacing.

"Mr. President, sovereignty is not a new demand. All of the treaties signed with the federal government guaranteed sovereignty to the tribes. This has never been upheld. The Supreme Court has defined reservations as 'dependent domestic nations.' No one is sure what that means. The Indians are sovereign by treaty, but not independent. What is a domestic nation? The treaties guaranteed sovereignty, but the United States government does not allow tribes to exercise sovereignty. For example, my tribe wants to build a new high school on the reservation. We have the money, the land, everything. But we can't build it until we get permission from the Bureau of Indian Affairs and the Department of Education. If nothing else, we should be able to run our reservations ourselves, just like cities and towns do."

"Sheldon, things cannot continue like this. Something must be done. We need to reform the bureaucracy in this country." The president looked determined.

"Yes, sir, I agree. What do you suggest?" asked Sheldon.

"Why don't we privatize the bureaucracy?" asked the president. "There is so much inefficiency in the bureaucracy and no incentive to change. If we privatize it, there will be an incentive to make a profit. Bureaucracy will have to become more efficient. Maybe that is the best way to solve this problem."

"With all due respect, Mr. President," said Sheldon gravely, "I would have to disagree. Often the best way to make a profit is to cut costs. If that happened, there would be less incentive to actually find the missing trust funds or to help the Indians. I can't see a privatized bureaucracy fighting for Indian rights to fish and hunt in our historic grounds. Essentially, I believe there are some things that should be done by the government, even if it is less efficient."

The president just sighed and shook his head.

Points to Ponder

Agree or disagree with the following statements, and give your reasons:

1. The bureaucracy in this country is bloated, inefficient, and a waste of taxpayer money.

2. Civil servants have too many protections.

3. Without civil service protections, presidents could gut programs that help a great many people but do not agree with that president's agenda.

4. Although the Indians in this country have been treated badly, for the most part their treatment was no worse than the treatment of other groups.

5. It is unrealistic to expect the government to account for all of the funds that have been held in trust for the Indians over the past hundred years.

6. The Indians have been granted special status in this country for too long. It is time they were treated like other Americans.

7. It is harsh but true that some people will continue to have babies until someone, like the government, steps in and forces them to stop. This is in the best interest of the country.

8. The major problem with the bureaucracy is the fact that Congress does not give them specific instructions.

9. It should be easier to fire someone who works for the federal bureaucracy.

10. The president's idea of a union with no strike ability is a reasonable way to reform the bureaucracy. It wouldn't solve all of the problems, but it would be a good start.

11. Our government policy toward the Indians is very similar to Hitler's treatment of the Jews.

12. Iron Triangles are inconvenient, but a protection of minority rights. They are part of the checks and balances on the government.

13. The best way to solve the "Indian problem" would be to give them sovereignty over their lands. If the reservations were treated like cities, Indians could solve many of their own problems.

14. Sovereignty isn't in the best interest of the Indians or the country. Many reservations are on inaccessible wasteland where there is no viable economy, so the Indians will continue to need help.

15. While Indian gaming has helped some tribes, overall it is bad for the Indians and the country.

16. The president is right: we need to reform the bureaucracy in this country by privatizing parts of it. This will lead to greater efficiency.

Essay Questions

1. In spite of the fact that most bureaucrats are qualified and hard-working and the bureaucracy is actually highly efficient most of the time, the bureaucracy is hated in this country. Discuss this phenomenon and the reasons for it. How would you solve the problem?

2. One of the problems with the bureaucracy is fighting over turf. For example, the FBI, CIA, and other intelligence agencies are extraordinarily reluctant to share information. How would you resolve this problem?

Chapter 14

Who Will Judge the Judge?:
The Judiciary

J orge Escalente sat down with his coffee and smiled at Charles. "How are you and Judith this morning?" he asked.

"Good morning, Jorge," answered Judith. "Maybe you can bring some sense into this discussion. Charles here thinks we should take on the Johnson case. I don't think we should touch it. What are your thoughts?"

"Well, you know, Congress and the public are really starting to get upset; they think we've been doing too much public policy . . . ," began Jorge. He stopped speaking as Charles snorted.

"Congress should read the Constitution or *The Federalist Papers* sometime. We are doing our job. We're evaluating the laws passed by Congress and the states and deciding if they meet constitutional scrutiny," Charles said emphatically.

Jorge shook his head. "You know, Charles, I haven't been on the Court long, but the longer I'm here, the more convinced I am that we should hold to original intent. Cases like *Roe*, where the Court makes public policy, just don't seem to be what the Founders wanted us to do. I can see us essentially usurping the powers of Congress almost completely if we don't stop this."

"Oh really, you two," said Judith. "You know that as long as Congress refuses to legislate on hot-button issues, we have to step in to give the country direction. I don't like it any more than you do, Jorge, but when there are conflicting decisions at the lower court level, and Congress does not want to get involved, then we owe it to the country to get involved, no matter what your feeling about activist courts."

"Besides," interjected Charles, "you're just like the rest of us. You said what you needed to in order to get confirmed. You can't honestly tell me that you told the full truth to the Senate. I seem to remember you presenting yourself as a moderate with no opinion on judicial activism. It's amazing how you formed opinions on that issue as soon as your butt got on this Court."

Jorge sat with his mouth open, trying to formulate a reply. Judith jumped in to save him, saying, "Jorge, you have to keep in mind that Charles looked those senators in the eye and told them he had never given any thought to the constitutionality of *Roe*. Just because he fudged the truth, he assumes we all did."

Before Jorge could comment, Charles butted back in. "You know, we could debate this all week. I want to know if I have your support to grant *cert* in *Johnson*. Judith won't support it, partially because she's opposed to anything I want. I felt with you being new here, you wouldn't be inclined to just do something because it's the way it has always been done. I think it's time we had a debate about this issue."

Judith shook her head. Jorge sighed. "I realize that this is an important issue, but I just don't know if this is the right case. *Johnson* is arguing that it is unconstitutional for state judges to be elected solely because the Constitution specifies that states must have a republican form of government. To my mind, that simply means that the states must have a government that rests on the consent of the people. *Johnson* is arguing that means state constitutions should be similar to the federal Constitution, and thus state judges should be appointed by the governor and approved by the upper house of the state legislature. The argument makes no sense as far as I'm concerned. If the states must have a republican form of government, that would say to me that electing judges is constitutional.

By that logic, appointing judges, or even justices, is not republican. Face it: the public had no say in our appointments. The president nominated us, and the Senate confirmed the appointments. At the federal level, the judiciary is not in any way republican. To my mind, the more important issue is whether or not state-level judges should be elected, if that affects judicial impartiality. Also, federal judges serve for life. Most states have term limits on their judges. Considering how many judges are elderly, I don't think we should tell the states that they can't fire judges who are senile. As a matter of fact, there are those who argue some of the federal judges should be fired because they're too old."

"Okay, so you agree with me that we need to address this issue," responded Charles.

"Yes, we need to address the issue of the election of state judges. There are problems with the process. When more than a third of state judges say that campaign contributions affect their judgment in cases, there is a problem. But, and this is a big but, I don't think *Johnson* addresses the issue." Jorge looked troubled.

"And what are we all discussing so earnestly this morning?" asked Fred, who had just entered the room.

"Mr. Chief Justice, good morning," replied Jorge, jumping up from his seat. Charles and Judith smiled, adding their good-mornings.

"Jorge, sit down," said Fred. "I may be chief justice, but here at breakfast I'm just Fred. Now what's got you all hot and bothered?"

"The *Johnson* case," murmured Jorge.

"Why am I not surprised?" asked the Chief. "Charles is trying to rope you into supporting *cert* so that he can get on his high horse. You look like you're bothered by this. Tell me your concerns . . . and no, Charles, I don't want to hear from you. I know where you stand on this. It's okay, Jorge; tell me what you're thinking."

"Well, sir, it's complex. I agree that we need to address the issue of whether or not justice is served by electing state judges. But I don't think that this case has legal merit, it doesn't address that issue, and I also have a problem with the judicial activism issue. States will start screaming that we're interfering with federalism. The Tenth Amendment gives all other powers to the states. The Constitution only mandates that states have a republican form of government, not that their government mirror the federal Constitution. If we decide that the election of state judges is unconstitutional we will be destroying a major part of federalism. I sympathize with *Johnson* and agree with Charles that this is a serious problem. I just don't know if I can support this case. And then there is also the whole issue of judicial activism, which I'm still uncomfortable with. Also, there is racial equity. Less than 15 percent of judges are people of color. If we go to appointing judges at the state level, it is likely that we will get judges that look more like America. Face it, citizens don't vote for judges of color." Jorge sighed and looked at his cup of coffee.

"Well, Jorge, I'll take your last point first. The Court has been activist since Marshall made his decision in *Marbury v. Madison*. Whether or not the Founders wrote activism into the Constitution, tradition has given us that right. And unless Congress wants to take responsibility and legislate on hot-button issues, or amend the Constitution to eliminate that power from us, the Court will be activist. Now, as to whether or not *Johnson* is directly on point, that doesn't really matter. You haven't been here long enough to know how we work. If we want to deal with the issue, we can twist the case. You're right: the arguments in *Johnson* are not on point. But we can find the justification if we want to. Now, as to federalism and the Tenth Amendment, that is a valid point. But the relationship is constantly evolving. States screamed bloody murder with the civil rights decisions, saying that they violated the Tenth Amendment. But we also have a national supremacy clause in the Constitution. We can definitely get involved in this question, if that is what at least four justices want. We can grant *cert* and then engage the issue. So, basically, there is no question that we can get involved in this if we want." Jorge nodded his head. "You have to decide if you want to support this application for *cert*. I can tell you that Charles is willing to twist arms, blackmail, and trade votes to get what he wants."

Jorge laughed, along with Charles and Judith. "You're joking," said Jorge. "Blackmail, trading votes, twisting arms? The Supreme Court doesn't work like that, does it?"

"Actually, unfortunately, sometimes it does," said the chief justice wryly. "Sometimes that is the only way to get things done. For example, you and Charles seem to feel very strongly about the issue of electing judges at the state level. But Judith obviously does not. I would imagine Sam and Sherry don't feel strongly about it either. But I know they're trying to get support for issuing *cert* for *Duke*. So what is going to happen is that Charles, if he can't get support any other way, will tell Sam and Gary that he'll support *cert* for *Duke* if they support *cert* for *Johnson*. Then, when it comes time for the decision, there will be more backroom dealing."

"You know, Jorge," Judith smiled an apology to Fred for interrupting, "I hadn't considered the issue of elderly judges in relation to *Johnson*. That is a whole different can of worms, and I don't know if we want to bring that into the mix. There are a lot of people in the country who feel that federal judges should have a term limit, in spite of the Constitution."

"Judith, we'll come back to that," said Fred. "Right now I want to make sure Jorge is okay with how we decide which cases to take."

Jorge shook his head. "I can't believe decisions of this magnitude are made in such a way. We're talking about fundamental rights and the Constitution. And you're telling me these decisions are being made by justices trading votes, just like in Congress or a local PTA meeting?"

Judith smiled. "Jorge, you only served at the federal court level. If you had served on the appeals level, you would know that this happens all of the time. It is sad, but on many issues, vote trading goes on. I don't think there will be trading going on in *Duke*, but it is likely that votes will be traded on *Johnson*. We each have our issues that we feel are important, and so we're willing to trade votes to get an issue on the agenda. *Duke* raises important issues."

"Did I hear you say *Duke*?" asked Sherry, who had just walked in. "What is going on? Are we deciding *Duke* before hearing argument?"

"No, Sherry, you know we don't do that here," replied Fred. "We're explaining to Jorge that there are politics involved here, no different than in any other branch of government. Charles wants his support to issue *cert* for *Johnson*, and I used *Duke* as an example of when votes would be traded."

"We're going to issue *cert* on *Duke*, Fred. I've got the votes lined up already. I really didn't have to work hard, the issue is so intriguing. Even Judith supports me on this," said Sherry smugly.

"And another thing you'll learn after you've been here a while, Jorge," said Fred wearily, "is that sometimes we must avoid a case, in spite of the fact that some of the justices want to address it. In my opinion *Duke* is incendiary, and we should refuse *cert*. But my vote doesn't count any more than yours, and we will have to get involved in this issue. And no matter what we do, we will piss off parents."

"Come on, Fred, we piss off people on a regular basis. *Duke* raises important issues about parental rights and responsibilities. Too many parents are raising their children with racist values. The Dukes not only taught their children white supremacy, they encouraged their kids to 'stand up for their rights' and attack people of color. I agree with the state that these actions were child abuse and the children should have been removed from the home. And yes, I feel that this was appropriately classified as criminal action, no different from beating their kids. The criminal conviction of the Dukes for child abuse should stand." Sherry glared at the other justices, waiting for one of them to contradict her.

"Sherry, I know you feel strongly about this. I also find the Dukes' beliefs offensive. However, I don't know if I want us to get involved in these aspects of parental rights," said Charles. "For example, my sister is, in my mind, a little nuts. She is a vegan and is raising her kids as vegans. This is not vegetarian, this is absolutely no animal products. No eggs, no leather shoes, no chocolate milk. Now, to me, this is not a healthy lifestyle. But she has the right to raise her kids the way she wants. If we limit parental rights in *Duke*, shouldn't we also limit my sister's right to raise her kids as vegans? Where do we draw the line?"

"And what about vaccinations?" asked Fred. "If we involve the federal government in child rearing to this extent, can we still say that parents whose religion bans medical treatment can refuse to vaccinate their kids? Once we cross this line, we are in murky waters."

"We already limit parental rights," snapped Sherry. "It is against federal law for parents to circumcise their daughters. We call that female genital mutilation, and it is against the law in this country. Common law used to view children as the property of their parents, giving parents absolute rights over their kids. We've gotten away from that. If a parent beats their kid to death, that is against the law. We, as a society, have said that certain actions by parents are so offensive that they are not acceptable. I say that the teaching of racism and violent hatred to your kids is in the same category. It harms society as a whole, just like female genital mutilation, and we should tell the country this."

"Well, I can see that it is going to be a pleasant day today," said Gary as he entered. "Good morning, all. Sherry, when are you going to write your parents' handbook, telling everyone the things they can teach their kids?"

"And now we've heard from the peanut gallery," said Sherry, shaking her head. "Gary, I don't want to legislate everything a parent does. But I do think we have to set some standards."

"Well, if the measurement is the good of society, then you have a problem," said Gary. "For example, it is not in society's best interest that the Quakers are pacifists. In times of war, we need every able-bodied man—sorry, Sherry—every able-bodied person, to serve this country. But the Quakers do not support any type of military action. So, by your logic, we should tell the Quakers that they must serve in the military during times of national emergency. One of the fundamental beliefs of this country is freedom. People came to this country to have the freedom to practice their beliefs without government interference. You are advocating drastic government interference in the ways parents raise their children."

"Yes, I am," replied Sherry emphatically. "In my mind, this is no different from the Court telling schools that they couldn't force children to pray in school. We have to allow freedom for everyone. But freedom is not absolute; there are limits. And one of the limits should be that you cannot teach your children hatred that leads to violence."

"But Sherry," said Fred reasonably, "almost anything you teach your kids could fall into that category. For example, if you teach your kids tolerance for all things, people will say you're violating freedom of religion. If you are a Christian, your religion teaches you that you should try to spread your religious beliefs. You should try to convert other people. But that would violate teaching tolerance. And given today's problems, I can see parents being prosecuted for raising their children as Muslims. I can see some prosecuting attorney arguing that Islam is a religion of hate and violence, so raising a child as a Muslim would violate the law. Essentially what you're getting at is you want to control people's thoughts. No one can do that. My fear here is that we will make a decision that is impossible to enforce."

"It is not just that it would be impossible to enforce. It would be confusing to the nation. There would be no clear guidelines of what was acceptable and what was not," said Gary. "It would be the pornography decision all over again. We know what is acceptable, but the community does not. And, Sherry, while I understand why you want to do this, you need to understand that what the Dukes did was already illegal. Incitement to violence, accessory before the fact, these are crimes that the Duke parents were guilty of. We don't need to add the child abuse count. And the Dukes can also be held responsible in civil court; relatives of the boy who was killed can sue them. I don't like the idea of putting people in jail because of their beliefs. That just smacks of Hitler or Stalin. It is un-American."

"Excuse me," Jorge interrupted. "I would like to get back to *Johnson*. Judith said that the Constitution allows for lifetime service for federal judges. I disagree. Article Two, Section One, says that judges shall serve during good behavior. Nowhere does it say lifetime service. The fact that it doesn't say a specific number of years of service causes many people to assume that the Constitution says lifetime service. It does not. If there is a judge who is old, becoming senile, or no longer able to hold to a high professional standard, in my opinion, we should just stop paying them. But no, we don't do that. If a federal judge has committed a crime, been convicted, and is sitting in jail, Congress holds impeachment hearings. And if a federal judge is senile, Congress keeps paying their salary, just refusing to assign cases to that judge. Why? This is not good behavior. So just fire the person. If we're going to be upholding the Constitution, we should at least go by what the Constitution has to say."

Dead silence followed Jorge's statement. Finally Fred cleared his throat and said, "Well, Jorge, that is one way to look at the issue. But you must remember, the Constitution is a living document. As such, it is open to interpretation and tradition. Traditionally that clause has been interpreted to mean that federal judges serve for life. Can you imagine what would happen if we took your interpretation? The president would immediately try to remove Charles from this Court because he's senile. We know he's not senile, at least not most of the time"—the others chuckled, including Charles—"but the president disagrees with Charles and would like to see him declared senile. Lifetime tenure is our protection, the only way we can ensure that we can make unpopular decisions. Can you imagine *Brown v. Board of Education* being decided the way it was if justices could be easily removed?"

"Also, Jorge," said Gary quietly, "the words of the Constitution are not enough. We need to think about the intent of the Founders. It is clear that their intent was that federal judges serve for life."

"I don't think we want to go there, Gary," said Judith. "I hate to sound like you, but once you start down that road, you're in trouble. We can't know the intent of the Founders on many things. If the Founders intended the federal judges to serve for life, they would have specified that in the Constitution. There is some merit to Jorge's position. Having said that, I don't think we should go down that road. As Fred said, tradition is important. The Constitution does not give us the power of judicial review, but we've exercised that power since *Marbury*. Likewise, tradition says that we serve for life. I think the system works well that way."

"Actually, Judith," said Charles with a grin, "I'll play devil's advocate. In some countries judges are appointed for twenty years. We could do that here. For example, you're appointed to the federal court and can serve for twenty years. At the end of that time, you can be reappointed. If you're an idiot, or have early-stage Alzheimer's, then you don't get reappointed. However, if you're really good, let's say you've served fifteen years of your term, you can be appointed to the Court of Appeals for twenty years. And you can be reappointed or even promoted to the Supreme Court for twenty years. Let's face it: most justices don't serve twenty years. And if you're really good, you can be reappointed. That would be a way to resolve the problem of the senile judges." Charles grinned again, waiting for Judith to respond.

"Well, yes, Charles, that works in some countries," said Judith tolerantly, "but the thing to remember is culture. Every culture is different. Our culture is accustomed to believing in lifetime tenure for federal judges, and any change in that is likely to be negative. Fred is right; if we had your system, I would never have been appointed to the Supreme Court. My decisions at the lower levels disturbed some people. That alone would have been enough for them to refuse to reinstate me at the Court of Appeals level, where I served twenty-five years. My decisions on women's issues particularly troubled many in the Senate. But, because the senators knew I held my job for life, those decisions weren't as big an issue during my confirmation hearings for the Court. They knew they couldn't get rid of me. And feminists lobbied the Senate so much that the senators couldn't vote not to confirm me. But to have to face that every twenty years? I don't think so."

"Judith is right," said Gary. "We have to have job security if we're going to make controversial decisions, like the one we face in *Collins*." This statement was greeted with a groan from all of the other justices. As they were groaning, Sam, Susan, and Donald joined the breakfast.

"*Collins?*" asked Sam. "Donald and I were just discussing it. I think it will be a fascinating case. I love it when there are conflicting rights in a case. Freedom of speech versus the right to a fair trial . . . I just love it."

Donald shook his head, as did several of the other justices. They knew Sam too well.

Jorge spoke up, "I don't see the conflict. I thought it was resolved years ago. Freedom of speech is no different in this case from freedom of the press. If the press has the right to cover a trial, if that is in the public's best interest, then freedom of speech should also be in the public's best interest. Collins is wrong when he asserts that allowing participants in a trial to write a book corrupts the trial. The jurors, the prosecutors, even the judge have freedom-of-speech rights. We cannot tell them that they cannot write books about their experiences during a highly publicized trial. Jurors and judges can do what is right during the trial and then write about it afterwards without impacting the trial."

Charles laughed out loud. "Don't you see any inconsistency in your beliefs? You agree that campaign donations to state judges corrupts the process, but you don't think it corrupts the process if there is a book deal? I can see jurors thinking about ways to present themselves in their books rather than thinking about the evidence. We've seen that in televised trials. There is a lot of posturing on the part of the judge and attorneys. Why won't the same thing will happen with the jurors?"

"It's different," said Jorge. "*Collins* is arguing that it is impossible to get a fair trial if the participants are able to make money off of their participation by writing books. That essentially the trial will have been turned into a commercial transaction. That is not so. All of the participants will be doing their job. It is only later that they will write a book. Yes, some of them will try to present themselves in the best light, but they're already doing that now. Campaign contributions to judges happen before the trial and influence the way the judge rules. One happens before the fact, the other happens after the fact."

"Well, looking at how televised trials have evolved, I just don't know," said Susan. "In the ones I've seen, everyone is playing to the cameras. They want the coverage. I can see the same thing happening in the books. I can see jurors jockeying to be foreman, not saying things out of fear of how they will be presented in books." Seeing the confusion on the faces of her colleagues, she tried to explain. "For example, when I was in law school I was a juror in a murder trial. The defendant was a white man accused of killing a black man. The prosecutor tried to paint this as a crime of racism, even before we had hate crime legislation. Many of the jurors agreed with the prosecutor that this was a racial crime, a white man killing a man because he was black. But this was a simple robbery of a drug dealer by another drug dealer. I argued that race had nothing to do with this crime. I convinced some of the other jurors. We still convicted, but I came across as being racist. But race had nothing to do with that case. Now, if those deliberations were being recorded for a book, I wouldn't have been able to make that argument without being portrayed to the public as a racist. I would have thought twice before making that argument. It is no different from our deliberations. We deliberate in isolation, keeping no records, so that we can speak our minds. I grant you that we will all leave our papers to the Library of Congress, and there will be memoirs about the deliberations, but they will not be made public until all of us are dead. Can any of you honestly say that you would like our deliberations to be published shortly after we make our decision? That is the point *Collins* is trying to make."

The other justices reflected on the points Susan had made. "What do you think of the televised trial in Texas?" asked Gary. "I mean, it wasn't enough that they televised the entire trial, they also put a camera in the jury room to cover the deliberations. I can see that one coming to us for review, with the defendant arguing that he couldn't get a fair trial because the deliberations were televised. I mean, with him being accused of such a horrendous murder, I can't see any of those jurors arguing against conviction with their friends and neighbors watching."

"Well, fortunately, we don't have to engage that issue until the appeal comes to us," said Fred, cutting off discussion of that subject.

Donald cleared his throat. "What about the Douglas case? Have any of you given that any thought?"

Sam shook his head. "I really haven't looked at it much. What are the issues?"

Donald said, "This is the so-called 'duped-dad' case. Mr. Douglas decided that he did not want to pay as much child support as the court had awarded his wife. So he challenged the judgment, saying he doubted the kids were his. DNA tests showed that one of the children was not his biological child. Mr. Douglas then asked to be relieved of any child support for that child and an abdication of all parental responsibility. The trial judge, appeals court, and state supreme court refused Douglas's request. Essentially, Mr. Douglas had acted as a father for the child in question for more than seven years. He was the only father this child had ever known. Until the DNA test, Mr. Douglas appeared to be a loving father to this child. It is true that his wife was wrong to deceive Mr. Douglas about the paternity of this child. However, the child was not at fault. It is in society's best interest for that child to have a relationship with a father. Yes, Mr. Douglas is being hurt. But the child is the defenseless one here and the state supreme court, as well as the appeals court and the family court, felt that the interests of the child should be paramount."

Sam said, "Essentially the state is forcing this man to be a father to another man's child. That is wrong. Mr. Douglas is being, excuse my language, screwed with his pants on. He shouldn't have to pay child support."

"Sam, the man I called father was not my biological father," snapped Charles. "Parenthood is not necessarily about donating DNA. I agree, what Mrs. Douglas did to her husband was fundamentally wrong. However, the interests of the child must come first. This is for the good of the child and the good of society. I won't go into the potential financial problems if Mr. Douglas were allowed to refuse to pay child support for this one child. The bottom line is that Mr. Douglas had acted as a father to this child, from the day that child was born."

"So what you're saying," said Sam, "is that every father should have a DNA test done on the newborn child; otherwise, whether the children are his or not, he will be responsible for them for the rest of their lives."

"Sam, if I can decipher your pronoun use, essentially, if you accept that child at birth, yes, I do feel you are the parent for life," replied David. "Again, you must keep in mind the good of society and the child. You must also keep in mind that you don't have to be linked by DNA to have a loving relationship as a parent. If that were true, many families in this country would fall apart."

Points to Ponder

Agree or disagree with the following points, giving your reasons:

1. The Supreme Court has been making too many decisions that affect public policy. These are issues that should be addressed by Congress, not by a branch of government that is not elected.

2. Nominees to the federal courts generally say what is necessary to receive approval by the Senate, not what they really believe.

3. It corrupts the system to have state judges running for office.

4. Appointing state judges would be good for the country. If nothing else, it would lead to more persons of color as judges.

5. The Supreme Court twists cases around to impose their desires on the public.

6. It is wrong that vote trading, arm twisting, and blackmailing go on in the Supreme Court.

7. The lower court ruled correctly in *Duke*. Parents who teach violent racial hatred to their children should be charged with child abuse.

8. The decision in *Duke* was wrong. We cannot legislate what people can think or believe.

9. We have limited parental rights too much in this country. It should be a basic freedom to raise your children according to your beliefs.

10. Jorge is right: the Constitution does not explicitly give federal judges lifetime tenure of office. Congress should be able to just fire incompetent judges.

11. The tradition of lifetime tenure is a strong protection of minority rights. We should leave it alone.

12. As Charles says, minority rights could still be protected with twenty-year appointments to the federal courts, the way the system works in other countries.

13. In the conflict between a fair trial and freedom of speech, the right to a fair trial should prevail.

14. Allowing jurors, prosecutors, and judges to write books about note-worthy trials corrupts the system.

15. Televising trials, particularly the jury deliberations, is good for the country. It allows people to see how and why judicial decisions are made.

16. Televising trials corrupts the process. Trials need to be about justice, not about entertainment or show business.

17. The Supreme Court should uphold the decision in the duped-dad case. It is in society's best interest that the child have a father who pays child support, even if he isn't the biological father.

18. Hate crime legislation is bad for our country. It brings racism into situations where it doesn't necessarily exist, and it punishes people for what they think, which is wrong.

Essay Questions

1. Discuss the problems with and reasons for an activist judiciary. What recommendations would you make to deal with the problems associated with this situation?

2. How can we work to ensure a fair judicial system at all levels (local, state, and federal), while maintaining an independent judiciary?

Chapter 15

Social Safety Nets?:
Social Welfare Policy

G ood afternoon to my fellow Americans. From Washington, D.C.,
this is Gary Gladman, the voice of common sense in the nation's
capital. Today, while we're on the air, our members of Congress are discussing the latest bill to attempt to deal with the problems of poverty in
this country. I think we need to tell them just what to do. So I'm opening
up the phone lines for your comments. Remember, the number is 1-800-
COM-SNSE, or for those of you that don't know the alphabet keys on
your phone, the number is 1-800-266-7673. This is a toll-free call from
anywhere in the country, so you have no excuse for not calling and contributing. I remind you that, as always, the transcript of this show will
be sent to our members of Congress, so they will know what America
thinks about this subject, and maybe they will even get some ideas on
how to solve the problem. Jack, who is our first caller?"

"Gary, the first caller is Joan from Rochester, New York," replied Jack.
"Go ahead, Joan."

"Hi, Gary, thanks for taking my call. I want to say that I find it offensive
that it is so easy for some poor people to abuse the system. What I'm
talking about is how often they trade their benefit money for drugs. I'm

sorry, but I don't want my tax money going to pay for their drugs while their kids go hungry."

"Good point, Joan, but you should know that on this show, it is not enough to complain. Hell, everyone can complain. You also have to offer a solution to the problem. So, what would you do about it?" asked Gary.

"Well, one thing to do to make it harder to abuse the system is to give them food instead of money. Right now there is basically an ATM card. A friend of mine uses it, and she buys steaks and other expensive stuff. She trades this to her drug dealer. He sells the food to restaurants. I say instead of allowing her to choose what to buy, we give her food that the government has in storage—all the cheese, flour, beans, that the government has sitting in warehouses. When you go to pick up your food there will be some meat, but no more grocery shopping. If you don't like what the government is offering, get a job and buy what you want. We also need to do something about the drug addicts on welfare or other public assistance. So I say mandatory drug testing for public assistance. If you're on drugs, you don't get our help."

"Whoa, Joan, just a little harsh there, huh?" asked Gary. "I like the idea of limiting their ability to buy steaks, but assume I'm a welfare mother with three kids and also a little addiction to crack. You take away my social benefits, my kids starve. Is that what we want?"

"Not quite, Gary, but I also don't want a crack addict raising kids who will probably become junkies and perpetuate the cycle of poverty. I'd be willing to pay more in taxes for good drug rehab centers. If this mother goes through the program, she keeps her kids and her benefits. But if she doesn't want to quit drugs, she should lose her benefits and her kids. We make it too difficult for the state to take kids away from unfit parents. I don't care how much that woman loves her kids, that is not a fit environment for kids to be raised in." Joan's voice was beginning to sound angry.

"Well, who will raise those kids? As it is, we don't have enough people who want to adopt, and there aren't enough foster parents. What are you going to do with the kids?" asked Gary.

"First of all, we've got to make it easier to adopt. Granted, we want to ensure that the adoptive parents aren't child molesters, but other than that, why not allow gays to adopt, single parents to adopt, older parents to adopt? We make it too hard. And because the state makes it so difficult to permanently remove kids from their birth parents, many kids spend years in foster care. There are people willing to adopt these kids, but the system won't let them. Also, keep in mind, when these kids get adopted, the state no longer has to pay support for them, like they do for foster kids," Joan said vehemently.

"Okay, Joan, thanks for giving us something to think about. That was Joan from Rochester. Jack, who do we have that wants to respond to Joan?" asked Gary.

"We have Chuck from El Paso, Texas, on the line."

"Hi, Gary, Jack. I think that Joan had some good ideas. She should have thought it through better, though. That crack mother will keep having kids until we do something. I'm sorry, but if you're a drug addict, you're not using birth control. I want that woman sterilized so she's not bringing more kids into this world, kids that will be born with drug addictions. If she goes through rehab, instead of surgical sterilization, maybe do the implanted birth control. If she does clean up her life, she could eventually have more kids. But we've got a woman in our neighborhood, she's got six kids already, is pregnant again, has never been married, and she's collecting social benefits. I'm sorry, but she has no incentive to change. I'm not saying that she's typical, or that life on benefits is a piece of cake, but we're making it too easy. First of all, I want people on benefits to either be in job training or working. I also want better child support collection. If this woman was collecting child support from the fathers of her kids, she wouldn't need benefits."

"All right, Chuck—some good points," interrupted Gary, "but what if the fathers of those kids are in prison or dead or something? No money coming in there. Also, you want this woman to get a job. Who's going to take care of her kids while she's working? What kind of job skills does she have? If the economy is bad, who is going to hire this woman?"

"Obviously, Gary, if the father is dead he can't pay support. But one of the big problems today, at least in Texas, is the majority of women on benefits are not receiving child support. Not all the fathers are dead. We need better collection. Now, as far as who takes care of the kids: we need federally funded child care in this country. And think about this: some of the adults who are currently collecting welfare benefits could actually work in these child care centers. This would help out the community, and it would also give them skills that would help them get future jobs. Now, as for our crack addict, there are things she can do. If nothing else, she can pick up garbage on the highway in return for her benefits. There are a lot of jobs like that, where you don't need skills, and people who want government benefits can do those jobs. This won't solve the problem, but it will help."

"Well, Chuck, you've got some good ideas there, but I do think the Supreme Court might have some problems with the mandatory sterilization. That kind of goes against the grain," replied Gary.

"Actually, Gary," said Chuck, "look at your history books. In the 1920s the Supreme Court found involuntary sterilization constitutional. It was practiced in this country until the late 1970s. Then all those liberals in the ACLU got involved, protecting everyone's rights. I'm sorry, but a drug addict does not have a right to reproduce and bring drug-addicted kids into the world, kids that I will have to pay for." The studio resounded with the sound of Chuck slamming down his phone.

Gary chuckled and asked Jack, "Do we have anyone who wants to respond to Chuck?"

"Actually, Gary," said Jack, "I've got Juanita from Watsonville, California, and she's ready to come right through the phone. You go ahead, Juanita."

"Thanks, Jack. Gary, the woman from New York and the guy from Texas have obviously never been poor. Let me tell you, I have three kids. I work two jobs. My ex-husband pays a little child support. But here's the thing. When we got divorced here in California, the judge awarded me $2,000 a month child support, based on three kids and the cost of living here in California. Then George moved to Vermont and remarried. He has another kid with his new wife. He claims he can't find a job, but seems to be able to afford a nice house. He got himself a lawyer and went to court in Vermont. The judge there said that $2,000 a month was extortion and lowered his child support payments, in part because George claims he doesn't have a job. Now he is paying me $150 a month. I'm sorry, but that's not right. The judge in Vermont has no right to change what the judge here awarded. The Vermont judge does not know what it costs to live here in California. When I sent him a letter complaining, he wrote back that I should move somewhere less expensive to live. Right. I've got a decent full-time job with health benefits for me and my kids. The second job takes care of what George used to pay. I've got family in the area to help take care of the kids while I'm at work. I move, I have none of this. So, my recommendation is that all child support decisions are made in the area in which the custodial parent lives. A judge in another state or even county cannot overturn that judgment. If you feel that the support is too much, you have to appeal that in the county where the judgment is made. Yes, George would have had to fly back to California, but that is his problem. Right now, I'm faced with having to fly to Vermont to try and get this overturned. And believe me, I'm not the only single parent in this position.

"And I agree with giving food instead of food stamps. I've seen people in the grocery store using food stamps, and then they walk out into the parking lot and get into a BMW. Also—now this sounds a little wild— there are women all over this country who are collecting benefits. Train some of them in basic investigative techniques. They can track down the deadbeat dads like my ex and see if they're working under the table. Document this, and force these guys to support their kids. These women would now have job skills and other women, like me, would get their child support."

"Okay, Juanita, those sound like workable suggestions. We'll pass them on to our members of Congress. Thank you," said Gary. "Jack, who do we have next?"

"We have Tina from St. Petersburg, Florida. . . . Go ahead, Tina."

"Hello, Tina. We can always count on you for some good ideas. What are your suggestions today?" asked Gary.

"Gary, there are a lot of old people here in Florida, and many of them are poor. We need to have better elder care, state-funded assisted-living complexes for the elderly. One of the major things is to have all of their utilities and prescriptions at a controlled rate. The way to pay for this is to have means testing for Social Security. As it is, it doesn't matter how wealthy you are, you can still collect Social Security. So I say if you have an income of more than $200,000 you cannot collect Social Security," Tina said succinctly.

"The problem, Tina," replied Gary, "is that those wealthy people paid into Social Security. They expect to get back what they paid into the system. That is their money that the government is holding in trust for them. They will argue that they shouldn't have to give up their benefits just because some people didn't do adequate retirement planning. I don't know if I would disagree with them. You have to keep in mind that Social Security was always intended as a retirement supplement. We have too many people who didn't do any retirement planning and expect the government to take care of them."

"Gary," snorted Tina, "your attitude is typical, and, forgive me, totally wrong. Yes, Social Security was always intended as a supplement. But if you've been working at low-level service-industry jobs all your life, you can't afford to put any money into an IRA. You need to meet your current bills. As far as it being your money that the government is holding, that is just not true. If that were true, then you wouldn't get lifetime benefits. The majority of American retirees take much more out of Social Security than they put in. The bottom line is, people are just greedy. If you are wealthy, you don't need Social Security. This country's government and economic policies allowed you to make a great deal of money. You owe it to the country to give something back. When we've got people who worked hard all of their lives and are today making the choice between buying food and buying medicine, then there is something seriously wrong. We all need to do our part. Given that there are so few workers supporting retirees, we need to change our thinking about Social Security. Not everyone will be happy, but this is the best thing for our country."

"Well, Tina, you've given this some thought. However, I doubt it will be accomplished." Gary paused before continuing. "Keep in mind that retirees are the group most likely to vote. They will fight any changes in Social Security that will limit their benefits."

"Yes," replied Tina. "But you need to keep in mind that among the population of retirees, there are many more who are poor than are wealthy. They and their families can outvote the wealthy retirees. Keep in mind that the general working population would also be likely to vote for this, as it would mean fewer increases in the taxes we pay to support retirees. Also, we need to have more homeless shelters, but specifically for kids. So many teenagers are homeless, but they are afraid to go to shelters, where they face abuse."

"Good point, Tina. Thanks for contributing." Gary turned and looked at Jack. "Who's next for us, Jack?"

"We have Wilma from Detroit, Michigan. She wants to change the topic a little."

"Welcome, Wilma. What do you want to discuss? How are the Red Wings doing?" Gary was a big hockey fan.

"Good afternoon, Gary. I have no idea about those Red Wings. I'm not a big sports fan. I'm actually a social worker, so I know what I'm talking about. We've got to do something about homelessness. That is a major problem for this country!" Wilma waited for Gary's response.

"I agree. But what do you suggest we do? After all, you're the expert in the field. I assume you want more programs, more housing, more help for the homeless. How are you going to pay for it?" Gary asked snidely. He didn't like know-it-alls. Wilma wasn't going to come up with anything new.

"You can deal with that; I want no part of it." Wilma paused to catch her breath, and Gary shook his head, thinking, what is she talking about? A social worker obviously wants more homes and shelters. Wilma began to speak. "I'm really tired of seeing all of the mentally ill, the drunks, and the panhandlers. We actually have a great many programs to help them, but they don't want any help. They just make life miserable for hardworking people. We need to take some action on these people.

"The first thing I would say is we need to amend the Constitution to take some of the rights away from the mentally ill. As it is, we can't keep them in treatment. They have a constitutional right not to take their medication. This means that they have the freedom to become severely psychotic, threatening people and even attacking them. We need to look to the rights of the majority. Amend the Constitution so we can institutionalize these people. Keep them in institutions for at least a year, so that they become adjusted to their medication and get counseling. Then have a monitor permanently attached, so that they can be tracked down if they escape from the institution. That monitor stays on until their condition is permanently cured. For those who want to leave the institution after a year, or if the psychiatrist thinks they're ready to leave, they have the monitor and they are forced to take their medication. If we can develop a Norplant implant for birth control, we can develop the same thing for psychiatric medication. This implant is put in before the person can leave the institution. They must be checked every six months to make sure that the medication levels are right. With the monitor we can find them and make sure they get their meds checked. This will be in the best interest of society as a whole." Wilma paused to take a deep breath before continuing. Gary interrupted her.

"Wilma, this is really a radical proposal. People are going to say that this is too drastic, that there is no reason to limit the rights of people who are mentally ill. After all, they had no control over this physical impairment." Gary was in shock; he hadn't expected such a proposal.

"I don't care if it is radical. Every day I see people who have been hurt by mentally ill homeless people. Sometimes it is just shouting at someone, most of the time it is physical attacks. Yesterday I had to help a twelve-year-old girl who was beaten and raped by a local homeless man. This man has been in and out of institutions for more than twenty years. If the girl lives, she will be scarred for life. It is time we limit the rights of these mentally ill people. The bottom line is that everyone will be better off if these people get the medical help they need." Wilma's voice was beginning to show stress.

"Okay, Wilma, calm down," said Gary soothingly. "Obviously there are problems in Detroit, and something needs to be done. How are you going to pay for this program?"

"Actually, Gary, it would probably cost less than what we're doing today." Wilma's voice had returned to normal. "As it is, the government spends a great deal of money on the homeless, and the costs of my program would simply come out of that funding. When you add in the cost of the damage from the crimes committed by these people, the costs associated with bringing them into the hospital on a regular basis because they've called in that they're having a heart attack, the additional police needed to deal with problems created by these people, we would probably save money by putting them into mental institutions."

"Okay, I'll buy that. What about the homeless alcoholics or those who just want to be homeless? What would you do with them? You said earlier that you didn't like panhandling. What is your suggestion there?" asked Gary, wanting to keep this woman, with her controversial ideas, on the air.

"Well, Gary, these are people that choose to be homeless. They want to drop out of society. I say let them. Cut off all benefits to them. If they don't want to be part of society, then they shouldn't expect anything from society. Make panhandling a felony to stop these homeless people from harassing hard-working citizens. If they want to get out of their situation, they must be enrolled in school or a job-training program. I say that many of those decommissioned military bases be used to take these people out of the way. If they want to be permanently drunk, they can live in these camps and be drunk. Their families can send them the money for booze. This will give them a roof over their heads, food when they want it, and the opportunity to change their lives. We could offer counseling. They could work in these camps, learning job skills and hopefully turning their lives around so that they can reenter society. The bottom line is that I shouldn't have to worry about these people urinating or defecating on my property, harassing people coming to my office, asking them for money. These people claim they have the right to live as they like. I do too. Their rights end at my nose. I shouldn't have to put up with this. Neither should anyone else," concluded Wilma emphatically.

"Wow, Wilma, you definitely have some radical ideas. It seems to me like you want to go back to the way we were before World War II, when there were distinctions made between the worthy poor and the unworthy poor. The worthy poor were the people who lost everything in a fire or something, and the unworthy poor were those who were poor because of their own actions. We helped the first and not the second. Are you sure we should go back to this?" Gary asked cautiously, uncertain what else this woman might suggest.

"Yes, I am. Let's face it, too many people are just abusing the system. That is taking benefits away from the people who are honestly trying to get out of a bad situation. There is only so much money to go around. Shouldn't it go to those who will be helped out of a bad situation and then go to work, be contributing members of society? Why should it go to people who just want to live like animals? And we also need to stop mollycoddling the drug addicts. Personally, I think that after the third time you've been caught using drugs you should be put to death, but I doubt the country would put up with that. But I do think that we should round up all of the addicts and put them into camps far away from anyone. They wouldn't be able to get drugs, and they could then clean up. This way they won't be robbing people to get drugs, they won't be killing or raping people while high, they won't be giving birth to drug-addicted babies, they won't be absorbing all kinds of tax money. We've made it too easy for these people, and it's time to stop." Wilma waited for Gary's response.

"You know, Wilma, some of your suggestions may have some merit, but I have to say, I really get tired of you wealthy white conservatives who just want to stop all social programs. You may be a social worker, but I wouldn't want to be one of your clients. You need to develop some compassion for people who haven't had your advantages. It is difficult to accept, but some people have hard lives and turn to drugs to deal with it."

Wilma chuckled softly. "White boy, your prejudice is showing. My skin is dark black. My daddy was a sharecropper in Alabama. He came to Detroit during World War II. I was born here in the ghetto, and I've never considered voting Republican. I do have a college education, because I worked three jobs while going to school. I make less than $50,000 a year. I'm not a wealthy white Republican. I'm a poor black Democrat. But that doesn't mean that I like what I see when I look around the streets. You think that a bad childhood is an excuse? My seven brothers and sisters and I shared two bedrooms. Our apartment wasn't on the wrong side of the tracks, it was under the tracks. Our school was so underfunded it was laughable. And from the time I was six my oldest brother was raping me. That went on until I was thirteen and pregnant. If anyone had a reason to turn to drugs or alcohol it was me. I didn't. You have to take responsibility for your own life. There are no excuses. Life is not meant to be easy; life is a struggle. You deal with your problems. You don't drown them in chemicals. Yes, it is hard, but it can be done. And believe it or not, many drug addicts come from nice homes, with money, and two parents. They just are looking for an easy high. So, Gary, take a look at your preconceptions. Many of us are fed up with this permissive society, and it is time for a change. Have a good day." Wilma hung up the phone.

"Well . . . all right," Gary stuttered. "Wilma's right. I do assume that people who advocate drastic social changes are rich white conservatives. We all have our stereotypes. I was wrong. I'd like to apologize to you, Wilma, for insulting you. I'd also like to say I'm sorry for what you went through as a young girl. I admire the fact that you surmounted all of those problems. I admire you. I don't know if I agree with your solutions, but I respect your views and admit that you probably know more about the situation than I do, sitting here in my studio, living in a neighborhood with no homeless people. Jack, who do we have on the line? Hopefully it won't be someone who will make me look like an idiot again."

"I don't know about that idiot bit, Gary. Seems to me that is kind of easy to do. But on the line now we have Bernard from Des Moines, Iowa," Jack said, grinning.

"Hi, Gary. Just so we know who we are, I am a white male, a Republican, but middle-class. I have to say that Wilma has a point. We need to change attitudes in this country. Too many people think that society or the government owes them something. Drug rehab, medical care, a job, school, whatever. That is bull. The government owes you safety. It is the job of the government to protect this country from invasions, and to protect people from crime. Other than that, you're responsible for your actions and your life. People think it is the government's responsibility to help out the poor. Maybe. I can accept some level of government help. But what I can't accept is the attitude that goes along with it. When I was young, my parents were poor. There were social programs that would have helped, but my parents wouldn't accept that. They were too proud. It was considered shameful to take charity. You turned to family members to help out, rather than relying on society. That attitude is gone these days. Too many people flaunt the fact that they're getting government help. We need to bring back shame. Put the names of welfare recipients in newspapers, on billboards, so that people know who's on welfare. This way if I know my neighbor is on welfare, and he all of a sudden has a brand-new car, I can report him. Also, many people wouldn't want others to know they were getting help; this would encourage them to change their lives rapidly. I realize that sometimes it is hard. But we need to get rid of the attitude that the government owes us a certain standard of living. Also, I think we should ban immigrants from collecting any social benefits. If they come here, they better be able to support themselves. I would like to limit our immigrants to those with a skill, like Australia does, but I doubt that is feasible with our porous borders. But I do think that immigrants either should support themselves or return to their home country."

"Well, there are some advantages to your plan, Bernard," said Gary. "But what if I'm an immigrant and a fire takes my home, clothes, and car. I lose my job. This is the worthy poor person. Why shouldn't I get some benefits until I get on my feet?"

"Because you haven't lived here long enough to get the benefits from our taxes. Keep in mind, there are charities that will help you. But our government programs should go to the people who have voted them into being and paid for them. Essentially, if I moved to China and couldn't make it financially, the Chinese would not help me out. They would throw me out of the country. We need to adopt that attitude here," said Bernard with strong conviction.

"Okay, good point, Bernard. Thanks for sharing your thoughts with us." Gary turned to Jack. "Who do you have on the line now, Jack?"

"Gary, we have Pammy from New York City, and she says she wants to give the other side of the issue." Jack raised his eyebrows meaningfully.

"Hello, Pammy, you're on the air. What do you have to say?" asked Gary.

"Hi, Gary. Like Bernard, I'll let you know that I'm white and middle-class, but I'm a liberal Democrat. I think it is time to bring some sanity to this show. Some of these suggestions have been just too much. What we have to realize is that capitalism dictates that there will always be a segment of society living in poverty. What we need to do is decide what that level should be. Currently the poverty line is an income below $18,000 for a family of four. Can you imagine trying to live in New York City on that income? We need to dramatically increase the minimum wage and have it reflect the cost of living in the area. Obviously the cost of living in New York City is much higher than in a small town in Mississippi. The minimum wage and the official poverty level should reflect that. All college expenses should be tax-deductible. We should also make the use of mass transit tax-deductible, so that people will have an incentive to get out of their cars. We need a great deal more low-income housing. The government could give massive tax breaks for the contractors and owners to give them an incentive to build low-income housing. We also need more job training for the poor, better access to child care. And as for humiliating those who are collecting benefits, why shame me? I'm collecting benefits because my ex isn't paying child support. Put his face on a billboard proclaiming he's a deadbeat. I liked the idea of making some welfare mothers private eyes. If we give them a small percentage of the child support they help collect, they have a great incentive to find the deadbeats. We need to stop punishing people for being poor. No one wants to be poor. If we implement these programs more people will live better lives, and that will help society overall. It will also lower crime rates. And before you ask, I would pay for this by dramatically increasing the tax on the very wealthy, the highest 5 percent of society. Businesses might complain about the higher minimum wage, but this will enable more people to buy products. That helps business in the long run. Also, businesses that move their factories overseas and then bring products back into this country should be taxed heavily, to make up for the loss of jobs here. We also need to use the revenue from higher income taxes to fund better mental health programs, better veterans' benefits, and pay doctors to practice in poor areas. We should have a limited form of socialized medicine in poverty-stricken areas. The government could waive student loan payments for doctors who practice in these areas."

"Okay, Pammy, those are some decent suggestions. Thanks for calling. Jack, who is next?" asked Gary.

"Gary, we have Alma Mae from West Virginia."

"Good afternoon, Alma Mae. Obviously, today Jack is in the mood to flirt with the women callers. After you're done, I hope we'll start to hear from the other half of the population. What do you have to say about the problems of poverty in this country?" Gary returned Jack's dirty look.

"Well, Gary, I want to go back to what Bernard was talking about. We need to bring back responsibility in this country. Too many parents aren't raising their kids right, and it's partly the fault of the government. These kids can't be disciplined. I remember my dad spanking me on two occasions. I never pulled either one of those pranks again. If I was doing something wrong, most of the time all my dad had to do was raise his eyebrow and I would stop. That respect isn't there anymore. Last week my daughter, who is sixteen, stayed out all night. I took her car keys and grounded her for a month. She turned around and reported me to Child Protective Services. I've just gone through an entire week of investigation because of that. Now if I try to discipline her, she'll just report me again.

"We've got to do something about this. The bottom line is that while they were investigating me, CPS was not investigating someone who was beating or otherwise abusing their children. If there's someone in my situation, where the child reported the parent for some frivolous reason, then CPS should punish the child. Send her to a boot camp for two weeks, and when she gets back, she will realize how good she has it here. Right now kids have too much power. We need to give parents more power and instill a sense of responsibility among our kids. Look at the Harlem Boys' Choir. Those kids come out of some of the worst ghettos in this country, but they have a sense of self-discipline, they have respect for people and property. I want to see the Golden Rule in every classroom, and I want parents to have more control. At the same time, I want parents to have responsibility also. I have a friend who doesn't care what her son does. If her son puts graffiti all over a building, she should pay for cleaning it off. If he cuts school for a week, send her to jail. This will ensure that she starts paying attention to what he is doing. She will start disciplining him. If she doesn't, then take the son away. She's not doing anyone any favors by not disciplining her son. She's turning him into someone who will not obey society's rules. Essentially, if we have a parental responsibility law, more parents will exercise control over their kids, and this will prevent these kids from becoming lifelong criminals."

"Well, Alma, I agree that there are problems here, but I don't know if I want to be held responsible for everything my son does. But thank you for calling. Jack, who do you have on the line now? Is it another woman you're chatting up, or is it a man?" asked Gary.

"Jack, I can't help it if some days it is mostly women who call. But you're lucky. I have Phillip from Provo, Utah, on the line."

"Hi, Gary. Gary, one of the problems is that convicted criminals can't get jobs. This means that many of them give up and return to crime. One way to deal with this is to have the government hire some of the criminals. For example, burglars could be hired to show how to make your home more secure, hackers could give advice on computer security, forgers could do something similar. But most criminals don't want to help; they like their lives. We need to make prison so harsh that people don't want to go back. We need to bring back the chain gang, have many more crimes qualify for a three-strikes law, get rid of any type of convenience in prison. It is appalling that some prisoners live better, with better food, medical care, and leisure time than decent, hard-working citizens. Make prison bad enough and people won't commit crimes, because they won't want to go there.

"Now, this would help deter the present generation from crime, but it won't help those who are already criminals. Some of them want to change but society won't let them. The others just do not want to change. It is harsh, but I say we write off that entire generation. Find a nice island somewhere in the middle of the ocean and put the criminals there. Give them the supplies they need to build homes and plant food, but remove them completely from society. Many of them will never change; they will just keep preying on law-abiding citizens. This has to stop. It is harsh, but it is the only way to end this cycle. Keep in mind, Australia was originally colonized by convicts, and many of the original settlers in this country were convicts. They can either build a new society or kill one another off. But they will stop terrorizing our society. I realize this would entail an amendment to the Constitution, but I think it is worth it."

"Okay, Phillip, that is definitely something to think about. Unfortunately, our time is up for today. I'd like to thank everyone for calling in. As always, transcripts from this show will go to Congress, so that our elected representatives will know what you're thinking. We will be back tomorrow with another timely topic."

Points to Ponder

Agree or disagree with the following statements, and give your reasons:

1. Joan is right—there is too much abuse in the welfare system. A new way must be found to distribute food for those in need.

2. There should be mandatory drug testing in order to receive any social benefits.

3. We need to make it easier to permanently remove children from their parents' care.

4. If you want social benefits like welfare, birth control should be mandatory. Maybe not sterilization, but at least implanted birth control.

5. The solution to the problems of poverty in this country is better education and job training. With that, we will not have anyone living in poverty.

6. If you want social benefits, you should have to work. If nothing else, you could do litter removal or clean up the parks. This will help instill a sense of responsibility and a work ethic.

7. We should return to mandatory sterilization of society's misfits. This would benefit them and society as a whole.

8. We should make it a law that a judge cannot change child support unless that decision is made in the area that is the primary residence of the children. What happened to Juanita is fundamentally wrong.

9. We need to give parents more control over their kids. Having CPS take the kids to boot camp for a few weeks would help parents tremendously.

10. We should have a means test for Social Security. Too many greedy people are abusing the system.

11. We do too much for the elderly as it is. They just need to learn to plan for their retirement better. If they haven't, it should be up to their families to take care of them.

12. Wilma is right: we need to limit the rights of the people who are mentally ill and homeless. They are costing society too much in care and for fighting crime. It would be better for all of us if we institutionalized them.

13. We should be able to force the mentally ill to take their medication for the good of society.

14. Wilma is wrong: homeless alcoholics and drug addicts should not be put into camps. They should be allowed the personal freedom to live their lives as they please.

15. Those who are voluntarily homeless are part of our society, so they shouldn't be put into camps. We just need to learn to be more tolerant and build more public bathrooms and homeless shelters.

16. It is absurd to consider making panhandling a felony. If you don't want to give a panhandler money, you don't have to. We should just let them be.

17. We should go back to making a distinction between the worthy and unworthy poor.

18. We need to reinstill values of personal responsibility, pride, and shame for taking welfare.

19. Immigrants should be banned from collecting any benefits.

20. Pammy is right: the solution to poverty is to have more programs to help the lower classes.

21. No program is going to stop crime. Sending criminals to Australia and the American colonies didn't stop crime in Britain, and it wouldn't work here.

22. Prisoners have too many rights.

Essay Questions

1. Discuss the difficulties of formulating and implementing new social policy programs and how you could improve the system. Think about, among other things, federalism, the time it takes to respond to a problem, and the role of the media.

2. How would you solve the problems of poverty?

Chapter 16

The War Against Terror:
Foreign Policy and Defense

This is Paul Jameson for XYZ News. The movement of NATO, Russian, and Chinese forces continued today, without explanation from any of the governments involved. The president of the United States refused to comment on these troop movements, and the Department of Defense issued only a statement that the troop movements were part of a 'planned exercise.' The vast majority of the troops appear to be heading toward the Middle East, but some of the NATO troops are massing in Britain, and the Russian troops are gathering on the southern border of Russia, near the Islamic republics. Chinese troops seem to be heading to India and Pakistan. Given the heightened state of tension in the world, due to the numerous terrorist attacks in the past few years, these troop movements are striking many as ominous. In addition, the United Nations Security Council has been in a closed-door session all morning. The delegates have not taken a break, and, surprisingly, there have been no leaks as to what is being discussed. UN Secretary General Mohammed al-Hassani has scheduled a press conference to begin at noon eastern time, just moments from now. Hopefully he will be able to inform us of what the Security Council is debating. Here now is the secretary general."

"Greetings to all in the United States and around the world," began the secretary general. "Today is January 30, 2008, the seventy-fifth anniversary of Hitler's accession to power in Germany. The world would be a much better place if we had been able to prevent his coming to power. The majority of members of the world community would agree that we should prevent such a catastrophe from happening again. As you know, acts of terrorism have increased to unprecedented levels in recent years. These acts of terrorism have affected almost every country in the world, just as did Hitler's acts. The vast majority of the recent acts have been committed in the name of Islam. As you know, I am a Muslim. As a Muslim, I denounce these acts, as do most Muslims around the world. At the suggestion of the president of the United States of America, I began consulting with leaders of most of the countries in the world. The result of these consultations is a resolution that has just been approved by the Security Council in a secret meeting. The vote was not unanimous; Syria and Cyprus voted no. However, there is such a strong commitment to this resolution that it has already taken effect.

"As I speak, troops from NATO, Russia, China, and Japan, combined with other multinational forces, are mobilizing on the borders of nations that harbor terrorists or create an environment amenable to terrorism. They will invade and begin occupation of these countries over the next twenty-four hours. The military forces are under the leadership of Johan Weiss, one of Switzerland's leading military minds. As you know, the Swiss have been neutral for over five hundred years. The military forces, under the United Nations' mandate, will occupy the countries and depose the governments of these countries. It is important to realize that this is truly a UN operation. Although the suggestion came from the president of the United States, this is a multinational effort. There will be no specific country in charge, so this eliminates the accusation that a western capitalist democracy is trying to impose its will on the rest of the world, as was the accusation when the United States led the war against Saddam Hussein. This will also eliminate the need for a country to unilaterally interfere with another country viewed as sponsoring terrorism, as was the case with Israel's invasion of Lebanon. Obviously, the UN is going to need a large military force to carry out this resolution. Therefore, I strongly recommend every country institute a military draft, so as to be able to contribute military personnel to the multinational forces. The UN military commanders will evaluate all troops, to ensure that they are not actually promoting terrorism.

"As with the military, the UN representatives will be drawn from countries all over the world. The UN representatives will administer those occupied countries. A complete list of countries affected will be distributed after I have finished my announcement. The UN forces will continue to occupy these countries, and UN representatives will continue to govern them for a period of not less than fifty years. In addition, all funds tied to terrorism have now been frozen. This includes funds of terrorist organizations like the IRA, the PLO, al-Qaeda, and also all government funds of the countries that will be occupied. They include all of the funds of the Saudi royal family in banks outside of Saudi Arabia. Banks worldwide have agreed to refuse any transfer of funds from banks in countries where accounts have been frozen, and those currencies will no longer be recognized. In addition, the funds of private citizens living in those countries have been frozen. Banks worldwide have complied, so that even numbered accounts in places like Switzerland, the Cayman Islands, and Liechtenstein have been identified and frozen. These funds will be used to pay the costs of the occupation of the terrorist-supporting countries.

"Among the countries to be occupied are Saudi Arabia, Iran, Iraq, Israel, the West Bank and Gaza, Northern Ireland, Pakistan, the disputed province of Kashmir in India, and the Islamic republics of the former Soviet Union. There is overwhelming evidence that these countries actively support terrorism or create an environment where terrorism flourishes. As I said earlier, this is not a complete list; that will be available to you at the end of this news conference.

"Once these countries have been occupied, the UN representatives will begin administering them. Their first priority will be to assist the military in locating and destroying terrorist bases, arresting suspected terrorists, and destroying their weapons. They will then focus on addressing the causes of terrorism in those societies. Their focus is terrorism; this is not a means to stop all independence movements around the globe. The World Court will evaluate any political violence to determine whether or not it is terrorism or an independence movement. As a general rule, if innocent civilians, like schoolchildren, are targets of attack, then the court will consider it a terrorist movement, not an independence movement.

"For example, the terrorism in Northern Ireland is of long duration. The UN representatives will facilitate reconciliation between the Protestants and the Catholics in Northern Ireland through education of the children. There will also be meetings between survivors of terrorist attacks from both sides, so that each can learn of the pain associated with the terrorist activity. Only through educating several generations of children to live together and break down the stereotypes learned in the home will the hatred be stopped. We will educate the populace on the harm done by terrorism. For instance, in the Middle East, those Israelis who support the settlement of the West Bank will be assigned to work with Palestinians who have lost their homes or members of their families. Only if the people involved in these situations realize the harm done will the violence stop. We will also ensure that people remain in place. You will not avoid this reeducation by leaving the occupied country and moving elsewhere. The Security Council has decided that we will take the necessary actions to stop terrorism. This we will do.

"In the Middle East, UN representatives will take over all aspects of governing. Israel will be occupied, as will the West Bank. The Israeli settlements in the West Bank will be turned over to Palestinians. Any Jews who choose to remain in the land set aside for the Palestinians will lose their Israeli citizenship. We will create a state for the Palestinians. The Israelis have a functional democracy. However, their constitution allows fringe groups to seat members in the Knesset. The Israeli constitution will be rewritten, so that when the UN leaves the country, a political party must receive at least 10 percent of the vote in order to have representatives in the Knesset. This will prevent the fringe groups from having such disproportionate influence on their government. We will adopt such policies wherever we occupy a territory. Monarchies like Saudi Arabia will not necessarily become democracies. However, there will be changes in their government to ensure that a reactionary king cannot undo the reforms implemented by the UN. One of the problems in the Middle East is the fact that, in spite of all of the technology associated with oil wealth, the societies are still tribal. The UN representatives will work to instill a sense of nationalism, to break down the tribal mentality. This will also be necessary in parts of UN-occupied Africa. Once a sense of nationalism is fostered, the people will be less likely to turn to terrorism to impose their will on others. Fundamentally, many of these countries are missing an important tool of survival: civil society. Civil society is all of those organizations like interest groups, citizen advisory boards, media outlets, sports clubs, hobby clubs, and organizations for people that are outside of government control. Civil society is a buffer between the people and the government, a form of checks and balances, if you will. We will build civil societies in the countries that the UN occupies.

"Throughout the Middle East, the UN will take control of the schools, mosques, and other institutions where hatred is spread. Moderate rabbis will teach in the synagogues and schools of Israel, and moderate members of the ulema, or body of mullahs, will teach in the schools and mosques in Moslem lands. We have a group of both Sunni and Shiite members of the ulema willing to step into the mosques and schools where needed. No longer will young men be taught that a non-Muslim is the enemy, that Islam sanctions the jihad, that women are nothing more than broodmares. If, as a result of the teachings of their parents, these students do not change their views, boarding schools will be established to isolate the children from parental propaganda. In any religion there is disagreement over interpretation of doctrine. However, in Islam lately there have been too many deaths of innocents defended by various interpretations of the teachings of the Prophet. This will stop. It must be realized that what is happening with Islam is not unique. Every major Western religion has gone through a period of political violence. In a sense, Islam today is going through their version of the Crusades. However, today we have weapons of mass destruction. That makes Islam's crusades far too dangerous for the world. I am certain that Islam, like Christianity, will work through this need for political violence and return to the religion that was promulgated by the Prophet. The actions endorsed here today are to ensure that there is a world population left when Islam has conquered its need for political violence.

"In all of these countries, the UN representatives will control the mass media. No longer will the ulema in Saudi Arabia censor the magazines, television, and radio. It is unacceptable that the mass media in that country is dominated by religious programming, mainly commentaries on the Koran. This is not to say that we are imposing worldwide censorship. The media from other countries will be allowed free access into the occupied territories and the ability to freely report on almost all aspects of the occupation. They will be limited in their ability to cover military exercises, so as not to put the military into danger. And this is not to say that the Western media will tell the rest of the world what is happening. The Chinese media will be invited to report on the changes in the Middle East, as will African media. *Al-Jazeera* does create some problems. This is probably the freest media outlet in the Arab world. They will be allowed to freely report on UN activities outside the Middle East.

"However, any reports on the Middle East will have to be cleared before being aired, so as not to help terrorists. In order to ensure that *Al-Jazeera* is able to report fairly, criticizing the United Nations in the Middle East if necessary, these reports will be screened by a group of professional reporters from South Africa, Singapore, and Brazil. These reporters will be fluent in Arabic, so that they understand what is being reported. In the past, *Al-Jazeera* has been criticized by some countries for showing Western democracies in a bad light or being too pro-Islamic. *Al-Jazeera* is doing its job as an independent news outlet; they are criticizing what they find wrong with governments and society. They will still be allowed to do this job, as long as they are not promoting or aiding terrorists. Likewise, Irish media outlets will be scrutinized to ensure that they are not promoting terrorist IRA activity. It is easy to say that what we are attempting here is to persecute varieties of Islam. That is not the case. I am a devout man; I am not declaring a war on the religious beliefs of Islam or any other religion. However, in the twenty-first century we must go beyond religion and live in an interdependent world. Therefore, all people must be exposed to the ideas and beliefs of others. Only in this way can we learn tolerance.

"Those members of the ulema who have made a career of teaching a fundamentalist version of Islam will be removed from their homes. The international science station in Antarctica has been dramatically expanded, and the fundamentalist ulema will be housed there. Likewise, there is housing for other teachers who have promulgated doctrines of hatred. These people will be housed, clothed, and fed, but they will be denied any form of technology. They will not have cell phones, tape recorders, or access to the Internet. They will not be allowed to spread their doctrines of hate.

"Accused terrorists will be tried by the World Court. They will be provided with defense attorneys provided by nations without indigenous terrorist movements. These attorneys will be thoroughly investigated to ensure that they have no ties to terrorism. They will be assured of anonymity, as will the judges. This will allow the defense attorneys to have access to secret intelligence material without fear that the members of the intelligence community will be targeted for reprisal. Likewise, the anonymity of the attorneys and judges will protect their lives and the lives of their families. We will not allow the World Court to be subject to the terrorism that has affected judges in some countries, like the judges in Colombia who attempted to stop the terrorism associated with drug dealing.

"Terrorists who have been convicted by the World Court will be jailed in a new international jail located in the Australian outback. They will spend their entire sentence in isolation, so that new networks cannot be formed while they are incarcerated. This is something we have learned from France, where the prisons were breeding grounds for terrorism. These terrorists will have no contact with the outside world. All medical care will be provided at the jail.

All guards at this jail, as well as at the international station in Antarctica, will be led by the Swiss. They will be assigned on a religious basis. For example, only Muslim soldiers will guard members of the IRA or other Irish terrorists. Only Catholics will guard Muslim terrorists, and

Hindus will guard the Jewish terrorists. For terrorists with no specific religious affiliation, like the Basque Liberation Army or the Japanese Red Army, the guards will be from Iceland. History has shown us that the only way to stop a committed terrorist is lifetime imprisonment in isolation. The modern terrorist movements started in imperial Russia in the late nineteenth century. Vera Figner, the leader of one of the terrorist movements, was not deterred by any of the punishments meted out by the government. Only when she was incarcerated in isolation and in harsh conditions did she stop her terrorist activities. This example will guide our decisions with today's terrorists. It also informs us: we will look at both men and women for terrorist activities. There will be separate prison facilities for the women terrorists, and the two genders will not be allowed to interact. Women guards from various countries will guard the women terrorists. There are some who will object that these punishments are too drastic, that we are violating fundamental human rights. However, these terrorists have violated human rights and have thus forfeited those rights. When you wreak havoc, death, and terror on innocent civilians, you forfeit the right to control your life.

"The various intelligence associations around the world have already begun cooperating by sharing knowledge about terrorists, and a worldwide terrorist databank is being assembled. At this time it is mainly a list of names with some fingerprints. It will be expanded to include fingerprints and DNA samples from all accused terrorists. This will allow us to identify family members of terrorists and single them out for special attention, to ensure that they are not also terrorists.

"There are many around the world who will see this action as a gross violation of human rights and national sovereignty. However, the World Court in The Hague has endorsed this action. The United Nations was created to prevent wars. For its first fifty years, it was not effective in its mission. We will be effective now. Let me be clear on this: the UN will arrest people suspected of promulgating hate, these people will be tried in The Hague, and they will be sentenced to live out their lives in Antarctica. This is in the best interest of world peace and security. There will be safeguards to ensure that this is not used just to silence political enemies.

However, given the fact that we have now had several terrorist attacks using biological or chemical weapons and one using a small nuclear device,
the world cannot survive without stopping terrorism. Let me also say
that this will not be limited to religious hate speech. It is unacceptable
that women in this country, the United States, a country that has given
birth to many of the freedoms people worldwide hold dear, cannot go to
a doctor without fearing that they or their doctor will be blown up or exposed to anthrax. If you disagree with abortion in the United States, then
use the court system to change the law; do not kill people to force your
views on them. This is an act of terrorism and will be treated as such by
the United Nations.

"Let me emphasize that this is not an attempt by the United States or
any other Western country to impose an economic system or a governing system on these countries, nor is it an attempt to impose a Chinese-
style system. It is a fact that not every culture will support democracy
or capitalism. Most Muslim countries believe in the umma, the community, and thus are less inclined to grant individual rights, as is normal in
Western-style democracies. There is nothing wrong with that. However,
these societies must learn that Islam is not incompatible with human
rights. We have a UN Declaration of Human Rights that will be enforced
throughout these countries. In those countries where the customs will
not support Western-style democracy, the UN representatives will work
with the people to ensure that a new form of government is developed
that reflects the society and customs of the people while ensuring a guarantee of human rights. This will be a form of government that protects
minorities and allows for diversity of opinion, as long as it is expressed
peacefully within the framework of the government.

"These occupations will last a minimum of fifty years for several reasons. First, it is important to educate several generations of children in
tolerance. That takes time. This will also allow for the older generation,
that generation that supports the use of violence, to die out. In addition,
this will allow the UN to establish a system of schools and an infrastructure in some of these countries. In several of the countries on this list,
the standard of living is abysmally low. The funds seized from terrorist

activities will pay to increase the standard of living. Part of the UN Declaration of Human Rights includes the right to a home, medical care, and other necessities. It is our feeling that clean water, electricity, and sewage treatment are part of these other necessities. We also will give medical care, including birth control, to all people living in these countries. It is unacceptable that one country, the United States, can force their views on women of the world, leading to thousands of deaths every year. The women of the world will be allowed to control their reproduction. We do know that economic problems contribute to hate groups. In many of these countries too many college graduates cannot get jobs. We need to create functional economies in these countries, economies that are not based on a single industry, such as oil.

"Obviously, this is not something that can be accomplished overnight. The UN will work with established governments. For example, I earlier accused the pro-life activists in the United States of acts of terrorism. If the U.S. government arrests and punishes these people, the UN will not step in. However, if the United States refuses to take action against these people, the UN will step in. Likewise, some countries are trying to catch the terrorists and extremists within their borders; Indonesia is an example of that. As long as the government of Indonesia is actively fighting against the terrorists within their borders, the UN will leave them alone. However, if Indonesia stops fighting the terrorists or is unable to continue to fight them, the UN will step in. We will not necessarily occupy the entire country, but we will take whatever actions are necessary to stop the spread of terrorism.

"Many of these countries have raw materials that can be exploited. We have often heard that the United States went to war against Iraq for oil resources. We have decided on a two-pronged approach to this problem. First, Western governments will subsidize alternative fuel source transportation. There will be electric- and solar-powered cars and buses, as well as trains developed in the West for use in their countries and eventually for export. This will be better for the environment and will relieve the dependency of these countries on the oil resources from the Middle East. Obviously this will take time, so the economies of oil-producing states will not be devastated overnight. The UN representatives running the governments of the oil-producing countries will allow the extraction, refining, and sale of oil to continue, using the profits to run the country and develop an infrastructure. The UN representatives will also use some of those funds to help these countries diversify their economies, so that when the oil reserves are depleted, the country still has a functional economy.

"After World War II, Europe was devastated. The United States stepped in with the Marshall Plan, which helped rebuild the economies of Western Europe. In a sense, this is like a Marshall Plan for the countries where poverty breeds terrorism. This plan is not applied solely to predominantly Muslim countries or countries in the Middle East. For example, if they so desire, countries in sub-Saharan Africa can participate in the economic development part of this plan, as a way to stave off terrorism, as can countries in Southeast Asia.

"The military forces of the United Nations in this program will have immunity from prosecution for most actions. Obviously, if a military unit massacres an entire village, such as happened at My Lai, the unit will be held responsible at The Hague. However, if in tracking down and destroying terrorists, some of their bombs kill or injure civilians, the soldiers will not be tried as war criminals. Unfortunately, in war, some collateral damage is inevitable. Rape, however, will not be tolerated. If the countries on this list do not fight occupation, the number of deaths will be dramatically limited.

"I strongly suggest that those countries I have listed here submit to occupation. There will be deaths over the next few days as the UN forces occupy countries. However, we have established a massive multinational force. If a country does not submit, we will take whatever steps necessary to ensure submission. That includes the possibility of the use of weapons of mass destruction. The world wants an end to terrorism, and the UN will see to it. This is an ambitious task we have set for ourselves. I ask for the help and prayers of all citizens of the world who are tired of living in fear of terrorism.

"Thank you, and good day."

The picture of the secretary general faded, and the face of Paul Jameson appeared on the screen. "Well, obviously the secretary general's announcement is unexpected and unprecedented. I'm joined in the studio by Professor Lisa Tormatelini, specialist in international affairs, and Danny O'Brien, former assistant to the secretary of state. We also have Robert Stephenson, from the White House. Lisa, Danny, your first reactions, please."

"Well, Paul, I have to say that this is an ambitious proposal," said Lisa tentatively. "I can understand why the president suggested it. Since he is at the end of his second term, he doesn't need to worry about being reelected. However, this is committing the United States, along with many other countries, to an extended international intervention. There are serious concerns here. The president obviously told the U.S. ambassador to the UN to vote in favor of this measure, but does he have the power to do this without prior congressional approval? Although this is not a declaration of war, which needs congressional approval, it is a long-term commitment of our military forces. If nothing else, I can see Congress refusing to fund the military in order to prevent our participating in this program." Lisa paused to collect her thoughts. Robert jumped in with a response.

"Lisa, Congress will have to realize that the president has made this commitment in the best interest of all Americans. If Congress refuses, the only thing that will happen is the UN will draw additional troops from other countries. This is going to happen. We in this country need to accept that fact and begin helping the UN to eliminate the terrorist threat to the world." Robert smiled in satisfaction.

"Actually, I like it," Danny said. "I'm of the same school of thought as the secretary general. Our rights are no use to us if we're dead. And I personally would advocate going further than the secretary recommends. Obviously we need to stop the antiabortion terrorists in this country. However, I would advocate putting all Muslims in this country into concentration camps until we can determine which ones support terrorism and which ones do not. Now, now, Lisa, before you have a stroke, think about it. My people are from Ireland, which apparently will shortly be occupied by NATO. The reason that the IRA is still alive is the fact that so many people are secret supporters. Until we're sure that the Muslims in this country do not support terrorism, we need to be safe. And yes, before you ask, I would also support taking action against all the Irish and Brits in this country to ensure that they are not associated with the terrorism in Northern Ireland. The bottom line is, if I'm afraid to leave my house, all my civil rights and civil liberties are meaningless."

"Danny, I don't even know where to begin . . . ," said Lisa. "I agree that something must be done about terrorism. But we need to be realistic. The secretary used the example of Vera Figner as the terrorist who wouldn't stop. We can learn from that aspect of Russian history, but also another aspect: Chechnya. The Russians occupied that country for hundreds of years, and under the Soviet Union the Chechens were indoctrinated for seventy years with ideas about brotherhood and the goodness of Russians. However, that indoctrination was not effective. The Chechens have a strong independence movement, but some would call it a terrorist movement. If they have maintained their ideas for hundreds of years in spite of the strong indoctrination by the Soviets, I doubt the fifty years that the UN is advocating will make any difference."

"That is a good point, Lisa," said Robert. "But part of the problem there is the Soviets were trying to fundamentally change all aspects of Chechen culture in a void. The UN will work differently. They will work with elements of the Chechen culture, and that will work better."

Lisa just shook her head in disbelief. "Where will the line be drawn? Most of the world views the Chechen movement as a liberation movement, not a terrorist movement. Yet it appears that they will be under UN control. How will terrorism be defined? Will Colombia be occupied because the drug dealers are terrorists? Will Thailand and the Philippines be occupied because they allow teenage prostitution? Is that a form of terrorism? Will this be a way for the UN to start enforcing the Declaration of Human Rights everywhere? I mean, I would like the UN to stop the practice of female infanticide and female genital mutilation, but would the UN also occupy the United States because we do not offer housing for everyone? Is there going to be one moral and legal standard for the world? We don't even have such a standard in our country. Who will make these judgments for the world?"

Robert shook his head this time. "Lisa, you're imagining things. The UN will only occupy countries that support terrorism. They will not be implementing a worldwide standard of laws. You must agree that something has to be done to stop the spate of terror attacks around the world."

Before Lisa could reply, Danny jumped back into the conversation. "What about the militia groups, Robert? Will the militia groups in this country be classified as terrorist groups? There are constitutional limits to what we can do about the militia groups. Is the UN going to take care of this problem for us? I don't know how well that would go over with many Americans."

"If the militia groups start blowing up schools and daycare centers, then yes, they would be considered terrorist groups," snapped Robert. "But that doesn't mean the UN would come in. Keep in mind, if the country is actively fighting terrorism within their borders, the United Nations will not step in. And if the militia groups start to blow up schools, they lose a lot of the constitutional protections." Robert looked exasperated.

Jack cleared his throat, saying, "Robert, I realize that you don't have all of the answers, but let me ask you this: What is the UN going to do about interest groups? I can see some groups claiming that China should be occupied to ensure the freedom of Tibet or because of their one-child policy. Likewise, I can see others arguing that Brazil must be occupied because their policy on the Amazon amounts to environmental terrorism. The same could be said of the Japanese policy of overfishing parts of the ocean. I can see all kinds of interest groups worldwide demanding that the UN take action. Isn't this essentially working toward a world government run by the UN?"

"You're right, Jack, I don't have all the answers. My understanding is that the Security Council, in concert with the World Court, will make decisions on which countries to occupy and why they should be occupied." Robert paused before continuing. "While you seem to view those charges you just laid out as frivolous, many would see them as valid. The Security Council and World Court would make that decision."

Lisa reentered the conversation. "Robert, I don't hold you responsible for this policy initiative, but how can you justify this? Essentially, American troops are going to be going all over the world, taken away from their families, be wounded or killed, to fight terrorism, which is extraordinarily difficult to eradicate. How can we say this is in the best interest of the United States?"

Points to Ponder

Agree or disagree with the following statements, and give your reasons:

1. Terrorism is such a problem in the world that a program like this is necessary.

2. No matter what is done, terrorism will always be with us.

3. It is necessary for all people to give up some rights to fight terrorism. After terrorism has been eradicated, we can explore restoring rights.

4. In order to effectively change peoples' minds about beliefs that lead to terrorism, you will need a long-term program of indoctrination.

5. Soldiers should not be held responsible for "collateral damage" that occurs during war.

6. A plan such as the one outlined here would necessitate dramatic limits to national sovereignty. These limits would be worthwhile if they help to eradicate terrorism.

7. One person's terrorist is another person's freedom fighter. You can't distinguish between a terrorist and an independence movement.

8. Which countries would you put on this list of terrorist nations or nations that create a climate for terrorists? Why?

9. We need to work toward a world government. This would ensure that everyone in the world shared some basic beliefs, like the belief that we should not kill one another to settle political or religious differences.

10. This is just another example of the West imposing its belief systems on other countries, countries that are not willing to adopt Western life-styles.

11. It is wrong that the UN can drag us into a program like this, or other military engagements that we do not necessarily support.

12. It would be good if the UN became more involved in international affairs.

13. It is unfortunate that the veto in the Security Council currently prevents the UN from stepping in to stop aggression.

14. While terrorism is a problem, this is not the best way to solve it.

15. Indoctrination programs do not work; all they do is create another generation that hates.

16. Although we may find terrorism abhorrent, we have no right to step into other countries to go after terrorists.

Essay Questions

1. Formulate a policy to fight terrorism that is feasible, constitutional, and effective, hopefully while staying true to our ideals about ourselves and our country.

2. What actions should our government take to improve national security? To eliminate domestic threats?

Index

Printed in the United States
86385LV00003B/115-153/A